A Kentucky Educational Television Series

GED

MATH

Written By

Alan K. Garinger

600 Cooper Drive
Lexington, KY 40502
(606) 233-3000

First Edition

First Printing 1984 (Titled *Adult Math*)
Second Printing 1986 (Titled *GED Math*)

ISBN 0-910475-25-3   1 2 3 4 5

Kentucky Educational Television
600 Cooper Drive, Lexington, KY 40502

ABOUT THE AUTHOR

A native Hoosier and graduate of Ball State University, Alan Garinger has spent the last twenty years involved either directly or indirectly with adult education. For the past twelve years he has served as Community Education Director for the Muncie Community Schools (Muncie, Indiana). In this capacity, he is responsible for many traditional and non-traditional adult education programs. In this context he has written a variety of adult-oriented instructional materials. His interest in the use of the electronic media in adult education led to the development of a program designed to teach adult reading by telephone.

In 1966 he was chosen Indiana's Outstanding Young Educator. This selection was due, in part, to his work with adult learners. He has recently been appointed to serve on the Governor's Literacy Initiative in Indiana, a statewide effort aimed at improving all facets of continuing education.

Acknowledgements

The author wishes to thank the following people for their help in the creation of this book:

H. David Green, Community Education, Anderson, Indiana; David Wilkinson and Linda Warner, Department of Public Instruction, Indianapolis, Indiana; Joyce Carmichael, Adult Math Teacher, Sybil Haviland, Lab Technician, Washington Carver School, Don Whitehead, Director of Adult Education, and Wilma Ferguson, Teacher, Muncie, Indiana. Special thanks to the students, teachers, and lab technicians of all the learning centers in Muncie, Indiana, who put up with a lot of foolishness while I was working on this book.

Special thanks, also, to the members of the ADULT MATH Task Force who so willingly took the time to look at all of the videotapes and make suggestions for this book.

Mrs. Wilma Ferguson
Muncie, IN

Ms. Margaret L. Mims
Shawnee Adult Learning Center
Louisville, KY

Mr. Richard James Redmon
Durrett Learning Center
Louisville, KY

Ms. June Fox Cort
Lexington, KY

Mr. Chuck Guthrie
Murray State University
Murray, KY

Ms. Patricia R. Corcoran
Murray State University
Ft. Campbell, KY

KET Participants:
Mr. O. L. Press
Ms. Sandra H. Welch
Ms. Peg Griffith
Ms. Linda Lehtomaa
Ms. Connie Kohler
Ms. Donna Tremaine
Mr. William Wilson

The television series, ADULT MATH, was a team effort but without the special talents of each member it could not have been achieved. The members of the production team are listed below:

Host: David Wise
David: Richard Hamilton, School Administrator
Frank: Ken Jenkins, Teacher

Students with Primary Speaking Roles:
Todd: Howard Farmer
Bill: Monte Priddy

Sue: Donna Rimple
Martha: Freda Foh Shen

Other Students:
Gene Arkle
Shawn Darragh
Barbara Desiato
Gwendolyn Farris
Charles Hamlin
Barb Howard

Harriet Johnson
Ken Knose
Gralin Nailing
Susan Owens
Nancy Shane

Executive Producer
Sid Webb

Producers
Russell Farmer
Judy Tipton

Director
Russell Farmer

Associate Producer
Janet Whitaker

Floor Manager
Dennis Busher

Cameras
Jim Bugay
Duncan Hart
David Robinson
Robert K. Simmons
Tom Whitlock
Gale Worth

Lighting Directors
Mike Heaton
Steve Peckham

Audio Supervisor
Alan Owens

Audio
Mike Ramsey
Walter Scott
Roger Tremaine

Video Engineers
Hank Batts
Butch Houghton

Video Tape/Editor
Otis Ballard

Costumes/Props
Phyllis Culp
Cindy Sawyer

Electronic Graphics
Janet Whitaker

Special thanks: Mr. Don Witt, Adult Education Center; Mr. Louis Ceast, The Bistro Ltd., Lexington, KY; Lexington-Fayette County Parks Department, for providing locations and services used in the series.

Teacher's Introduction

The KET Adult Math Series is a blend of math principles and computational skills. It is a many-sided approach giving the student a host of different experiences with both the ideas and their applications.

This Videotext is more than just a workbook. It is a guide to the most efficient use of all the KET Adult Math material. It is written in 15 chapters to coincide with the 15 video programs. This guide, along with the rest of the KET Adult Math material — video programs and computer-based instruction — is designed so that mastery of all elements of the program will be swift and long-lasting.

While the video presentations are sequential, the individual sections of the programs are related and should be thought of as independent instructional aids. Proper use of this Videotext will steer the student to those concepts which require more study.

Each step of the way, intermediate goals will be attained, previous learning reinforced, with the final goal being a greater understanding of the most troublesome subject matter in adult math, fractions.

The Design

This series deals primarily with fractions as they relate to the rational sharing of numbers and related topics. Each video program is supported by a chapter in this Videotext. The programs are presented in three segments with a reinforcement break between them. These individual segments can be thought of as single-concept programs, and used individually as review material for students who have completed the series.

Getting the Students Ready

A comfortable facility with the basic operations of whole numbers is something of a prerequisite for achieving the fullest understanding of this series.

It would be wise to review those whole number operations before starting students in this math series. Of special importance is the understanding of multiple factors in whole numbers. A student who has the ability to sense common factors of two or more whole numbers will benefit more quickly from the series. However, because the programs revolve around number relationships, students will receive a great deal of practice in multiplication and division which will probably lead to increased speed and accuracy when dealing with whole numbers.

Using the Videotext

While this text is self-scoring and designed in such a way that the students can set their own goals, teacher discretion is still as important as ever. Guiding the students toward positive outcomes requires the same kind, if not degree, of teacher judgment as in using any other instructional tool.

The Math

From the first program to the last, the idea of rational relationship of numbers is the major theme. Most adult material does not stress this element as fully as it is treated here. It may be necessary to relate this concept to the primary text material used by your class. The programs are general enough that there should be no difficulty in doing so. In fact the KET math series can be used to clarify difficult concepts of fractions found in almost any material.

Along with the rational family concepts taught, you will also find that there is emphasis on the number line. This is to lend a feeling of concreteness to the entire number system. If your students are unfamiliar with the number line concept, minimal orientation to the idea is desirable.

Teacher Preview

We recommend teachers preview all the programs before using them with students. The programs are dramatizations. As such, many allusions in the conversation referring to concepts will be more apparent to teachers than to students. As a teacher you will be able to expand on these "hidden ideas," when needed, to enhance the total value of the series.

Documentation

This series has been developed through the best thinking of many practicing adult educators and consultants. It has been field-tested and found to be a meaningful addition to the available material geared especially to the adult learner.

How To Use This Videotext

There are four steps to mastery in the KET Adult Math Series.

1 PREVIEW.

Before you view one of the video programs it is important for you to know what to look for on the television. Read the preview of each program.

2 COMPLETE THE GOAL SETTING EXERCISE.

This is a short test that you score yourself and complete a chart of the results. The chart will tell you things that you need to pay close attention to as you view the program. Study the vocabulary section so you will be more familiar with the terms as they are used in the program.

3 WATCH THE PROGRAM.

With the goal setting information you can watch the show more intelligently.

4 REACT, PRACTICE, AND EXTEND.

The next few pages in the Videotext contain examples like the ones used in the program, discussion of the vocabulary and further explanation of the rules and ideas expressed on the TV. There is also a cumulative checklist so that you won't forget the things you have learned up to now.

A Word or Two More Before You Begin

In this series, which is about fractions, there will be some different ways to look at the ideas of how fractions go together. You will need to remember some of the things you already know about fractions. If you have a fair understanding about the uses of fractions, the video programs will be more meaningful. For instance, look at the illustrations below. You have seen them before, but once more won't hurt, and it will give you a running start.

Fractions as a piece of something:

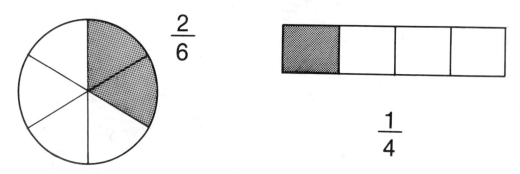

The bottom number of a fraction tells how many pieces something is cut up into. If something is cut into eight pieces, obviously there can only be eight pieces in the whole thing. In the first picture, a pie has been cut into six pieces. Four of them are missing. The fractional expression that talks about this situation is $\frac{4}{6}$ are gone and $\frac{2}{6}$ remain. You can see that the four-sixths and the two remaining pieces account for the whole pie.

Reducing

In many places you will be asked to reduce the answers to their lowest terms. Actually, fractions in their un-reduced form are quite proper. It is only that we have become accustomed to seeing them in their simplest form. If after the first two programs you are having difficulty with this process, look at "Rules for Reducing Fractions" on page 24.

You Are Now Ready
To Start the KET Adult Math Series.

TABLE OF CONTENTS

CHAPTER ONE:
Let's Be Rational About Fractions

1 **PREVIEW**

In this first program you meet some people who are studying math. The topic they are dealing with is fractions. They discuss the idea of fractions meaning a piece of a whole, and also the less well known idea that fractions are a member of a family of equal fractions. You will see the students discover ways to solve problems that have fractions in them.

By observing the students carefully in the video program, you will gain a greater understanding of fractions as they are used in everyday life. You will also gain a greater appreciation for the orderly nature of the number system.

Important Vocabulary

Common Denominator — The word "common" means "the same." You could ask, "What do these fractions have in common, $\frac{5}{8}$ and $\frac{3}{8}$?" The answer is, "Their denominators."

Common Factor — In dealing with fractions it is often necessary to find a number that will divide both the terms of a fraction. This number is called a common factor. In the fraction $\frac{9}{12}$, 3 is a common factor.

Common Fraction — The definition this videotext uses means any expression that represents a quantity less than one or a sharing of numbers that is less than 1/1.

Denominator — The bottom term of a fraction is called the denominator. It gives the "name" to that fraction. **Note:** Another form of this same word is used to name other things. The size of a bill is called its "denomination," and religious groups are referred to as a certain "denomination."

Factor — One way to think of a factor is to call it the number that will divide another number. Many numbers have several factors. For instance, 12 can be divided evenly by 1, 2, 3, 4, 6, and 12. Therefore 12 has these six factors.

Infinity — This is where numbers end. It is only an idea since, for our purposes, there is no such place.

Numerator — A fraction is made up of two numbers that go together in a special way. The top number, or term, is called the numerator. It can be thought of as the number of pieces being considered.

Rational Number Family — This term refers to the building of a series of fractions that are equal to one another. Sometimes it is called a fraction family or equivalent fractions.

Unlike Denominators — When the denominators of two fractions are not common, they are said to be "unlike." In order to add and subtract fractions, the denominators must be made common.

Think of these words as you watch the program.

2 GOAL SETTING EXERCISE

Solve these sets of exercises. Whenever necessary, reduce your answers to their lowest terms. (Answers on page 205.)

1. On the line below the illustration, write the fraction that is represented by the shaded portion of the drawing.

B.

C.   D.

_____   _____   _____   _____

2. Here is a number line. Write the fractions that are indicated by the points on the number line.

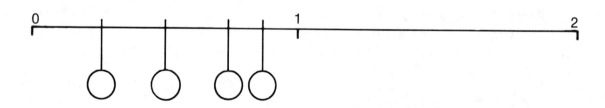

3. Write as many equivalent fractions as you can for each of the following fractions.

$\dfrac{1}{4}$ ___ ___ ___ ___ ___ ___ ___ ___ ___

$\dfrac{3}{8}$ ___ ___ ___ ___ ___ ___ ___ ___ ___

$\dfrac{2}{3}$ ___ ___ ___ ___ ___ ___ ___ ___ ___

$\dfrac{7}{8}$ ___ ___ ___ ___ ___ ___ ___ ___ ___

4. Add these fraction problems.

A. $\dfrac{1}{3}$ $+\dfrac{1}{3}$

B. $\dfrac{3}{5}$ $+\dfrac{2}{5}$

C. $\dfrac{3}{8}$ $+\dfrac{5}{8}$

D. $\dfrac{2}{7}$ $+\dfrac{3}{7}$

5. Subtract these fraction problems.

A. $\dfrac{3}{4}$ $-\dfrac{1}{4}$

B. $\dfrac{5}{8}$ $-\dfrac{3}{8}$

C. $\dfrac{7}{8}$ $-\dfrac{3}{8}$

D. $\dfrac{7}{16}$ $-\dfrac{5}{16}$

6. Add these fraction problems.

A. $\dfrac{2}{3}$ $+\dfrac{1}{5}$

B. $\dfrac{3}{8}$ $+\dfrac{5}{6}$

C. $\dfrac{5}{8}$ $+\dfrac{1}{3}$

D. $\dfrac{7}{8}$ $+\dfrac{1}{2}$

7. George worked $\dfrac{1}{2}$ hour overtime on Tuesday and $\dfrac{3}{4}$ of an hour overtime on Wednesday. How much overtime did he work altogether?

8. Mary had $\frac{3}{4}$ of a pound of butter. She gave her neighbor $\frac{1}{4}$ of a pound. How much did she have left?

9. You found that there was a leak in the lawnmower gas can. You knew that you had put $3\frac{1}{2}$ gallons in it, but you could tell that there were only $2\frac{1}{4}$ still in the can. How much had leaked out?

10. What is the least common denominator for the following sets of fractions?

A. $\frac{3}{4}$ and $\frac{5}{6}$ **B.** $\frac{2}{3}$ and $\frac{5}{8}$ **C.** $\frac{5}{6}$ and $\frac{3}{8}$

———   ———   ———

GOAL PROFILE

Put a check mark in the box that fits your situation.

When You Watch the Program

☐ A.   If you didn't miss any of the exercises, congratulations.

Pay close attention to the discussion of the number line and infinity.

☐ B.   If you missed any part of number 1, then . . . .

Listen to the discussion of fractions as parts of things.

☐ C.   If you missed any part of number 2, then . . . .

Notice the drawings of the number line. David and Frank refer to the number line often. It must be very important.

☐ D. If you missed any part of
       number 3, then . . . .

You need more experience with finding the equivalent in a fraction family. There is a sample of the equivalent chart used in the program on page 13.

☐ E. If you missed any part of
       number 4, then . . . .

Listen for the rules for adding fractions. There will be a chance for you to practice this skill after the program.

☐ F. If you missed any part of
       number 5, then . . . .

What rules are given in the program that will help you do better next time?

☐ G. If you missed any part of
       number 6, then . . . .

What does the program tell you about finding common denominators? What other rules are given that will help you solve problems that have unlike denominators?

☐ H. If you missed 7, 8, or 9,
       then . . . .

Listen for the clues that tell you the key words for solving fraction problems.

☐ I. If you missed any part of
       number 10, then . . . .

You need to watch with particular care the part of the program that deals with finding common denominators. If, after you have seen the program, you still have difficulty understanding common denominators, look at the chart on page 13.

3 NOW YOU ARE READY TO WATCH THE PROGRAM, "LET'S BE RATIONAL ABOUT FRACTIONS."

4 REACT, PRACTICE, AND EXTEND. (Answers on page 206.)

1. Here are four problems just as they were in the program. Can you solve them now?

A. $\begin{array}{r} \frac{1}{4} \\ +\ \frac{3}{5} \\ \hline \end{array}$
B. $\begin{array}{r} \frac{3}{4} \\ +\ \frac{3}{7} \\ \hline \end{array}$
C. $\begin{array}{r} \frac{2}{3} \\ +\ \frac{2}{5} \\ \hline \end{array}$
D. $\begin{array}{r} 6\frac{3}{4} \\ 5 \\ +\ 6\frac{2}{3} \\ \hline \end{array}$

2. Make a fraction family for each of the following fractions.

$\frac{1}{2}$ ____ ____ ____ ____ ____ ____

$\frac{1}{4}$ ____ ____ ____ ____ ____ ____

$\frac{1}{3}$ ____ ____ ____ ____ ____ ____

$\frac{3}{8}$ ____ ____ ____ ____ ____ ____

$\frac{5}{6}$ ____ ____ ____ ____ ____

3. Practice these examples that were not in the program. Put your answers in simplest form.

A. $\begin{array}{r} 1\frac{5}{8} \\ +\ 1\frac{3}{8} \\ \hline \end{array}$
B. $\begin{array}{r} 2\frac{7}{8} \\ +\ 1\frac{3}{4} \\ \hline \end{array}$
C. $\begin{array}{r} \frac{7}{8} \\ -\ \frac{1}{3} \\ \hline \end{array}$
D. $\begin{array}{r} \frac{3}{5} \\ -\ \frac{1}{7} \\ \hline \end{array}$

4. Vocabulary matching. Match the numbered words with the definitions.

1. Rational family   _____   **A.** The theoretical end of numbers.

2. Numerator   _____   **B.** Fractions of different denominators that describe the same size piece.

3. Denominator   _____

          C. The "top" term of a fraction.

4. Common denominator _____

          D. A list of several equivalent fractions.

5. Equivalent fractions   _____

          E. The "bottom" term of a fraction. The number that names the fraction.

6. Infinity   _____

          F. A number that both terms of a fraction can be evenly divided by.

7. Common multiple   _____

8. Common factor   _____   **G.** In fractions, a number that both denominators of a fraction problem will divide evenly.

          H. In fractions, the number that both denominators can be changed to.

Tips and Short Cuts

    Here are some examples of the operations used in the program. Look them over before you start to solve the rest of the exercises. You may want to remember where these examples are in your videotext so you can refer to them from time to time as you progress through the programs.

You saw the students solve problems that looked like this:

Case I: Adding fractions that have common denominators.

$$\frac{1}{8} + \frac{5}{8} = \frac{6}{8}$$ (6 and 8 have a common factor of 2)

$$\frac{6 \div 2}{8 \div 2} = \frac{3}{4}$$ (reduced)

Case II: Adding fractions that have unlike denominators.

Step One	Step Two	Step Three	Step Four

$$\frac{3}{5} = \frac{}{20}$$

$$+\frac{3}{4} = \frac{}{20}$$

$$\frac{3}{5} = ④\frac{}{20}$$

$$+\frac{3}{4} = ⑤\frac{}{20}$$

$$\frac{3}{5} = ④\frac{12}{20}$$

$$+\frac{3}{4} = ⑤\frac{15}{20}$$

$$\frac{12}{20}$$

$$+\frac{15}{20}$$

$$\frac{27}{20} = 1\frac{7}{20}$$

(reduced)

Step One: Find a common denominator. This can be done by finding a number of which both 5 and 4 (the two denominators) are factors. Or you can find a member of the rational family for $\frac{3}{5}$ that has the same denominator as a member of the family of $\frac{3}{4}$.

Step Two: Find the number you must multiply each denominator by to get this new denominator.

Step Three: Multiply the numerators by **this same number.**

Step Four: Add, then reduce if necessary.

Here is a subtraction model for the same operation:

Step One	Step Two	Step Three	Step Four

$$\frac{7}{8} = \frac{}{24}$$

$$-\frac{2}{3} = \frac{}{24}$$

$$\frac{7}{8} = ③\frac{}{24}$$

$$-\frac{2}{3} = ⑧\frac{}{24}$$

$$\frac{7}{8} = ③\frac{21}{24}$$

$$-\frac{2}{3} = ⑧\frac{16}{24}$$

$$\frac{21}{24}$$

$$-\frac{16}{24}$$

$$\frac{5}{24}$$

(in lowest terms)

REMEMBERING THE THINGS TO REMEMBER

- **Altogether** is a key to know when to add.

- **Compare** and **difference** are key words to know when to subtract.

- To add or subtract fractions, first find a common denominator.

- You add or subtract **only** the numerators.

- The rank of a member of a family helps determine what to multiply by to get a common denominator.

- Fractions are jealous. What you do to one term you must do to the other.

CUMULATIVE QUIZ (Answers on page 206.)

Solve. Reduce answers to the lowest terms.

1. $\dfrac{2}{3}$ $+\dfrac{7}{8}$

2. $\dfrac{3}{5}$ $+\dfrac{1}{8}$

3. $\dfrac{5}{6}$ $+\dfrac{2}{7}$

4. $\dfrac{3}{8}$ $+\dfrac{4}{5}$

5. $\dfrac{2}{9}$ $+\dfrac{5}{6}$

6. $\dfrac{5}{7}$ $+\dfrac{7}{8}$

7. $\dfrac{6}{11}$ $+\dfrac{3}{22}$

8. $\dfrac{9}{14}$ $+\dfrac{2}{7}$

9. $\dfrac{2}{3}$ $-\dfrac{5}{8}$

10. $\dfrac{3}{8}$ $-\dfrac{1}{7}$

11. $\dfrac{7}{9}$ $-\dfrac{1}{3}$

12. $\dfrac{5}{12}$ $-\dfrac{1}{6}$

13. $\dfrac{7}{8}$

$-\dfrac{2}{9}$

14. $\dfrac{3}{8}$

$-\dfrac{1}{4}$

15. $\dfrac{4}{5}$

$-\dfrac{1}{7}$

16. $\dfrac{9}{14}$

$-\dfrac{2}{7}$

17. $1\dfrac{1}{3}$

$+\ \dfrac{2}{3}$

18. $2\dfrac{1}{8}$

$+1\dfrac{4}{5}$

19. $3\dfrac{1}{2}$

$+1\dfrac{1}{7}$

20. $6\dfrac{1}{3}$

$+2\dfrac{1}{9}$

21. $3\dfrac{3}{4}$

$-1\dfrac{1}{8}$

22. $4\dfrac{2}{3}$

$-\ \dfrac{1}{6}$

23. 4

$-1\dfrac{3}{8}$

24. $2\dfrac{1}{3}$

$-1\dfrac{7}{8}$

WORD PROBLEMS (Answers on page 208.)

On these exercises you will need to decide from what is said whether to use addition or subtraction.

1. Todd removed three pints of paint from a gallon bucket. What fractional part of a gallon is left in the bucket?

2. Sue baked a cake for a friend's birthday. She cut it into 16 pieces. If each person at the party took just one piece and there was $\dfrac{1}{4}$ of the cake left, how many people were at the party?

3. Frank was grading papers for his class over the weekend. Friday night he graded $\frac{1}{4}$ of the papers. On Saturday he graded $\frac{1}{2}$ of them, and on Sunday he graded $\frac{1}{8}$ of them. Did he get them all graded? How do you know?

4. David lives 3 miles from the adult school. Frank lives $2\frac{1}{8}$ miles farther down the same road. Bill lives on the same road, but $\frac{3}{4}$ of a mile farther than Frank. How far does Bill live from the school?

5. Bill and Todd had an argument over which fraction was larger, $\frac{13}{16}$ or $\frac{7}{8}$. Todd said $\frac{7}{8}$ is larger. Is he right or wrong? By how much?

6. David is having topsoil delivered for his lawn. There were three truck loads delivered and dumped in his yard. One pile contains $2\frac{1}{3}$ tons, another is $2\frac{3}{4}$ tons, and the third is $3\frac{1}{8}$ tons. How much dirt has been placed in his yard?

7. Martha's neighbor's daughter is doing a science experiment. She is observing ants as they pile sand in one corner of her ant farm. She found out that each day they can pile $\frac{7}{8}$ of an ounce of sand, but each day she removes $\frac{1}{2}$ ounce from their pile. In 5 days, how much sand is in the pile? How much would the ants have moved if she had let them alone? How much sand did Jenny steal?

8.   A club was having a fund raising drive. They broke the members up into teams of different sizes to get the job done. The team that represented $\frac{1}{2}$ of the members generated a total of $400.00 The next team, which had $\frac{1}{3}$ of the members, brought in $200.00, and the smallest team, only $\frac{1}{6}$ of the members, contributed a total of $150.00. How much did the club collect?

My score on the Cumulative Quiz was _____ .
(number right)

EXTENDING YOUR UNDERSTANDING

A **common factor**, as you know, is a number that will divide both the numerator and the denominator of a fraction. This is the way fractions are reduced to their "lowest terms." When the only number that will divide both the numerator and the denominator is 1, the fraction is in its lowest terms.

CHART OF RATIONAL FAMILIES

$$\frac{1}{2} = \frac{2}{4} = \frac{3}{6} = \frac{4}{8} = \frac{5}{10} = \frac{6}{12} = \frac{7}{14} = \frac{8}{16} = \frac{9}{18} = \frac{10}{20}$$

$$\frac{1}{3} = \frac{2}{6} = \frac{3}{9} = \frac{4}{12} = \frac{5}{15} = \frac{6}{18} = \frac{7}{21} = \frac{8}{24} = \frac{9}{27} = \frac{10}{30}$$

$$\frac{1}{4} = \frac{2}{8} = \frac{3}{12} = \frac{4}{16} = \frac{5}{20} = \frac{6}{24} = \frac{7}{28} = \frac{8}{32} = \frac{9}{36} = \frac{10}{40}$$

$$\frac{1}{5} = \frac{2}{10} = \frac{3}{15} = \frac{4}{20} = \frac{5}{25} = \frac{6}{30} = \frac{7}{35} = \frac{8}{40} = \frac{9}{45} = \frac{10}{50}$$

$$\frac{1}{6} = \frac{2}{12} = \frac{3}{18} = \frac{4}{24} = \frac{5}{30} = \frac{6}{36} = \frac{7}{42} = \frac{8}{48} = \frac{9}{54} = \frac{10}{60}$$

$$\frac{1}{7} = \frac{2}{14} = \frac{3}{21} = \frac{4}{28} = \frac{5}{35} = \frac{6}{42} = \frac{7}{49} = \frac{8}{56} = \frac{9}{63} = \frac{10}{70}$$

$$\frac{1}{8} = \frac{2}{16} = \frac{3}{24} = \frac{4}{32} = \frac{5}{40} = \frac{6}{48} = \frac{7}{56} = \frac{8}{64} = \frac{9}{72} = \frac{10}{80}$$

$$\frac{2}{3} = \frac{4}{6} = \frac{6}{9} = \frac{8}{12} = \frac{10}{15} = \frac{12}{18} = \frac{14}{21} = \frac{16}{24} = \frac{18}{27} = \frac{20}{30}$$

$$\frac{3}{4} = \frac{6}{8} = \frac{9}{12} = \frac{12}{16} = \frac{15}{20} = \frac{18}{24} = \frac{21}{28} = \frac{24}{32} = \frac{27}{36} = \frac{30}{40}$$

$$\frac{2}{5} = \frac{4}{10} = \frac{6}{15} = \frac{8}{20} = \frac{10}{25} = \frac{12}{30} = \frac{14}{35} = \frac{16}{40} = \frac{18}{45} = \frac{20}{50}$$

$$\frac{3}{5} = \frac{6}{10} = \frac{9}{15} = \frac{12}{20} = \frac{15}{25} = \frac{18}{30} = \frac{21}{35} = \frac{24}{40} = \frac{27}{45} = \frac{30}{50}$$

$$\frac{4}{5} = \frac{8}{10} = \frac{12}{15} = \frac{16}{20} = \frac{20}{25} = \frac{24}{30} = \frac{28}{35} = \frac{32}{40} = \frac{36}{45} = \frac{40}{50}$$

$$\frac{5}{6} = \frac{10}{12} = \frac{15}{18} = \frac{20}{24} = \frac{25}{30} = \frac{30}{36} = \frac{35}{42} = \frac{40}{48} = \frac{45}{54} = \frac{50}{60}$$

CHART OF RATIONAL FAMILIES Continued

$$\frac{2}{7} = \frac{4}{14} = \frac{6}{21} = \frac{8}{28} = \frac{10}{35} = \frac{12}{42} = \frac{14}{49} = \frac{16}{56} = \frac{18}{63} = \frac{20}{70}$$

$$\frac{3}{7} = \frac{6}{14} = \frac{9}{21} = \frac{12}{28} = \frac{15}{35} = \frac{18}{42} = \frac{21}{49} = \frac{24}{56} = \frac{27}{63} = \frac{30}{70}$$

$$\frac{4}{7} = \frac{8}{14} = \frac{12}{21} = \frac{16}{28} = \frac{20}{35} = \frac{24}{42} = \frac{28}{49} = \frac{32}{56} = \frac{36}{63} = \frac{40}{70}$$

$$\frac{5}{7} = \frac{10}{14} = \frac{15}{21} = \frac{20}{28} = \frac{25}{35} = \frac{30}{42} = \frac{35}{49} = \frac{40}{56} = \frac{45}{63} = \frac{50}{70}$$

$$\frac{6}{7} = \frac{12}{14} = \frac{18}{21} = \frac{24}{28} = \frac{30}{35} = \frac{36}{42} = \frac{42}{49} = \frac{48}{56} = \frac{54}{63} = \frac{60}{70}$$

$$\frac{5}{8} = \frac{10}{16} = \frac{15}{24} = \frac{20}{32} = \frac{25}{40} = \frac{30}{48} = \frac{35}{56} = \frac{40}{64} = \frac{45}{72} = \frac{50}{80}$$

$$\frac{6}{8} = \frac{12}{16} = \frac{18}{24} = \frac{24}{32} = \frac{30}{40} = \frac{36}{48} = \frac{42}{56} = \frac{48}{64} = \frac{54}{72} = \frac{60}{80}$$

$$\frac{7}{8} = \frac{14}{16} = \frac{21}{24} = \frac{28}{32} = \frac{35}{40} = \frac{42}{48} = \frac{49}{56} = \frac{56}{64} = \frac{63}{72} = \frac{70}{80}$$

STEVE WISE SAYS:

1. There are as many numbers between one and zero as there are numbers from zero to infinity.

2. These numbers between one and zero are called **common fractions.**

3. Each fraction is a member of a family of which there are as many equivalent members as there are numbers.

4. A fraction has two terms:

   1 **numerator**
   2 **denominator**

5. In adding and subtracting fractions the common name (denominator) can be found by selecting members of the same family name from the families of the two fractions.

6. To add or subtract fractions, first find a common denominator.

7. You add and subtract **only** the numerators.

8. To find a common denominator, find a number that is a multiple of both the original denominators.

9. To find a new numerator, multiply the original number by the same number you multiplied the original denominator by to get the new denominator.

10. Short cut:
    A common denominator can always be found by multiplying the original denominators together.

11. **"Altogether"** is a key to know when to add.

12. **"Compare"** and **"difference"** are keys to know when to subtract.

13. Adding and subtracting mixed numbers can be done by considering the whole number and the fraction separately, then putting them together.

14. A fraction that has a numerator larger than the denominator expresses a quantity larger than 1.

CHAPTER TWO:

Fractions for the Forgetful

1 PREVIEW

In this program you'll see Martha discover a different way of quickly getting answers to addition and subtraction of fraction problems. She begins to realize that she has more knowledge about mathematics than she thought she did. Even better, she finds that she can use information she already has to solve problems.

You'll enjoy watching Martha become a better "number detective" as she learns to see number patterns and uses them to get answers she never thought she would.

As the program progresses you will find that you, too, will become more able to be a "number detective" and discover the math behind the story.

Important Vocabulary

REVIEW ALL THE VOCABULARY USED IN CHAPTER ONE. (PAGE 1)
All of the ideas used in chapter one are used in this chapter. You may or may not hear these words spoken, but the concepts are all there.

New Vocabulary:

Cross-Multiplication — This is a method in which, under certain circumstances, the numerator of one fraction is multiplied by the denominator of another. It has special meaning when dealing with the General Case Statement.

General Case Statement — As this term is used in this program it refers to a plan that can be used to solve all addition and subtraction of fraction problems.

Identity Element — In mathematics, this is a number that enters into the computation but has no effect on the outcome. In the case of addition the identity element is zero. More important for this program, the identity element for multiplication is one. Any number multiplied by 1 is itself.

Inductive Reasoning — You won't hear this term used, but it is the name for the thinking process that Martha uses to solve her problems. It is a way of looking at the parts of something and making some kind of judgment as to what the whole thing is just by what you can tell from the parts.

Reducing to Lowest Terms — When dealing with fractions, it is considered important that the final expression for a fraction is as simple a representation of the number relationship as possible. In these programs you will often hear that a fraction in its lowest terms is the first member of a rational family. Mathematically it means that the terms of a fraction have no common factor other than one.

2 GOAL SETTING EXERCISE (Answers on page 209.)

1. Here are some sequences of numbers. Continue the established pattern in the blanks indicated.

   A. 3, 6, 9, 12, ____ ____ ____ ____

   B. 4, 6, 5, 7, 6, 8, ____ ____ ____ ____

   C. $\dfrac{1}{2}$ $\dfrac{5}{6}$ $\dfrac{21}{18}$ $\dfrac{81}{54}$ ____ ____ ____ ____

   D. $1\dfrac{2}{3}$ $1\dfrac{11}{12}$ $1\dfrac{7}{12}$ $1\dfrac{5}{6}$ $1\dfrac{1}{2}$ ____ ____ ____

2. Try to solve these problems in your head. Just write the answers in the space provided.

   A. $\dfrac{1}{3} + \dfrac{1}{3} = \boxed{}$ **B.** $\dfrac{1}{3} + \dfrac{1}{4} = \boxed{}$ **C.** $\dfrac{2}{3} + \dfrac{1}{2} = \boxed{}$

3. Find a common denominator for the following sets of fractions.

   A. $\dfrac{2}{3}$ & $\dfrac{3}{7}$ ____   **B.** $\dfrac{3}{8}$ & $\dfrac{5}{12}$ ____   **C.** $\dfrac{4}{5}$ & $\dfrac{5}{7}$ ____
   \qquad\qquad C.D. \qquad\qquad\qquad\qquad C.D. \qquad\qquad\qquad\qquad C.D.

4. In number three above, how many possible answers are there to those questions?

   _____

5. List the factors for the following numbers.

   A. 14 - ____ ____ ____ ____

B. 36 - ____ ____ ____ ____ ____ ____ ____ ____ ____

C. 17 - ____ ____

D. 12 - ____ ____ ____ ____ ____ ____

6. What number can be multiplied by itself to get an answer that when the number **just** smaller is subtracted from it you get the number you started with?

7. Put the correct signs in the parentheses to make this number sentence read correctly.

   3   (   )   2   (   )   1   (   )   0   (   )   5

8. Find the missing numbers.

A.

$$\frac{1}{3} = \frac{4}{12}$$
$$+ \frac{\boxed{}}{4} = \frac{\boxed{}}{12}$$
$$\frac{\boxed{}}{12} = 1\frac{1}{12}$$

B.

$$\frac{\boxed{}}{5} = \frac{\boxed{}}{15}$$
$$+ \frac{\boxed{}}{3} = \frac{\boxed{}}{15}$$
$$\frac{\boxed{}}{15} = 1\frac{1}{15}$$

C.

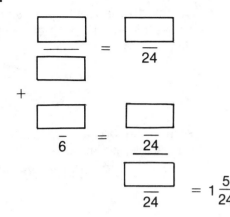

D.

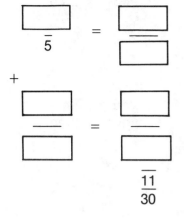

GOAL PROFILE

Put a check mark in the box that fits your situation.

When You Watch the Program

☐ A. If you got them all right,
pat yourself on the back.

See if you can see the relationship
between what Martha and David did in
this program and what was done in
program one.

☐ B. If you missed any part of
number 1, then . . . .

Study the things David did to get
Martha to become a better number
detective.

☐ C. If you missed any part of
number 2, then . . . .

Memorize Martha's models.

☐ D. If you missed any part of
number 3, then . . . .

Find out how Martha finds an answer
without thinking about common
denominators.

☐ E.   If you missed any part of
number 4, then . . . .   Review the rational families chart on
pages 13 and 14 before you see the
video program.

☐ F.   If you missed any part of
number 5, then . . . .   Remember program one and the
discussion on *infinity.* How do factors
get in a number in the first place?

☐ G.   If you missed any part of
number 6, then . . . .   Look at the definition of "identity
element." Be sure you understand David
when he asks Martha, "What did you do
with the 1's?"

☐ H.   If you missed any part of
number 7, then . . . .   Watch carefully to see how Martha
sees the relationship of numbers in
this program. How does she learn to
be a better number detective?

☐ I.   If you missed any part of
number 8, then . . . .   Ask yourself what patterns Martha
sees that will help you discover
patterns of your own.

3 NOW YOU ARE READY TO WATCH THE PROGRAM, "FRACTIONS FOR THE FORGETFUL."

4 REACT, PRACTICE, AND EXTEND.

Tips and Shortcuts

Now that you have seen the program, let's study Martha's models.

Model One

$$\frac{1}{4} + \frac{1}{3} = \frac{7}{12}$$

Can you see now that Martha, when she started, simply multiplied the denominators to get the new denominator and added them to get the new numerator.

Model Two

$$\frac{2}{3} + \frac{1}{4} = \frac{11}{12}$$

You get the new denominator the same way as before. Be sure to notice the order of the numbers in the denominator is different.

$3 \times 4 = 4 \times 3$

To get the new numerator she multiplied.

Model Three

$$\frac{2}{3} + \frac{3}{5} = \frac{19}{15} = 1\frac{4}{15}$$

This model is important because it shows that answers often need to be reduced. This is especially true with the General Case Method because frequently the denominator you use is not the least common denominator. Martha solved this problem by multiplying the denominators to get the new denominator.

$3 \times 5 = 15$

She cross multiplied to get the parts for the new numerator.

$(2 \times 5) + (3 \times 3) = 19$

$\frac{19}{15}$ is more than 1 because $\frac{15}{15} = 1$, therefore $\frac{19}{15}$ is $\frac{4}{15}$ more than 1.

Subtraction works the same way, except the two parts of the new numerator are subtracted instead of added.

Model for Subtraction

$$\frac{3}{4} - \frac{2}{3} = \frac{1}{12}$$

The denominator is found the same way

$$4 \times 3 = 12$$

$$(3 \times 3) - (2 \times 4) = 1$$

VOCABULARY MATCHING.   (Answers on page 210.)

1. Identity element   _____

2. General Case Statement   _____

3. Cross-multiplication   _____

4. Factor   _____

5. Lowest Terms   _____

6. Inductive Reasoning   _____

A. A number that will divide another number.

B. In a fraction, the expression in which the only common factor is 1.

C. A process of multiplying a denominator and a numerator in a fraction problem.

D. A thinking process that leads to the discovery of a principle.

E. The number in an operation that does nothing to the results.

F. A mathematical formula that always works.

1.   Now that you have seen Martha solve problems in her head, try to follow her example. Look at these problems and try to write down the answers. (Reduce if you can.)

A. $\frac{1}{4} + \frac{1}{3} =$ _____   **B.** $\frac{2}{3} + \frac{1}{4}$ _____   **C.** $\frac{3}{8} + \frac{1}{5}$ _____   **D.** $\frac{4}{5} + \frac{1}{8} =$ _____

E. $\frac{3}{8} + \frac{3}{7} =$ _____   **F.** $\frac{3}{4} + \frac{5}{8} =$ _____   **G.** $\frac{4}{9} + \frac{7}{8} =$ _____   **H.** $\frac{2}{7} + \frac{2}{9} =$ _____

I. $\frac{2}{5} + \frac{1}{9} =$ _____   **J.** $\frac{7}{8} + \frac{3}{4} =$ _____   **K.** $\frac{3}{5} + \frac{3}{7} =$ _____   **L.** $\frac{5}{9} + \frac{4}{5} =$ _____

2. Subtraction. (Reduce if you can.)

A. $\dfrac{1}{3} - \dfrac{1}{4} =$ _____

B. $\dfrac{3}{8} - \dfrac{1}{5} =$ _____

C. $\dfrac{4}{5} - \dfrac{1}{6} =$ _____

D. $\dfrac{2}{5} - \dfrac{1}{6} =$ _____

E. $\dfrac{3}{4} - \dfrac{1}{2} =$ _____

F. $\dfrac{4}{9} - \dfrac{1}{7} =$ _____

G. $\dfrac{2}{3} - \dfrac{1}{7} =$ _____

H. $\dfrac{7}{8} - \dfrac{5}{9} =$ _____

I. $\dfrac{4}{7} - \dfrac{1}{3} =$ _____

J. $\dfrac{2}{3} - \dfrac{3}{16} =$ _____

3. Put these fractions in proper order according to size starting with the smallest one first and ending with the largest. (You may have to compare them by using subtraction to know for sure.)

$$\dfrac{5}{8} \qquad \dfrac{2}{3} \qquad \dfrac{1}{9} \qquad \dfrac{5}{16} \qquad \dfrac{4}{5} \qquad \dfrac{7}{8} \qquad \dfrac{3}{4} \qquad \dfrac{4}{9} \qquad \dfrac{1}{2}$$

4. Find a fraction that when $\dfrac{1}{3}$ is subtracted from it the answer is still $\dfrac{1}{6}$ more than $\dfrac{1}{4}$.

My score on this exercise: _____ (number right)

The discovery process Martha used is called "inductive thinking." To use it Martha had to look at the various parts of the problem and find out how to solve the whole thing from these clues.

See if you can use the same process to discover a way that reducing a fraction can follow a similar process. Remember, David wouldn't let Martha tell him "how" she got the answer — just that she had a system.

$$\dfrac{10}{75} \qquad\qquad \dfrac{10 - 1,\ 2,\ 5,\ 10}{75 - 1,\ 3,\ 5,\ 15,\ 25,\ 75} \qquad\qquad \dfrac{10}{75} \quad \dfrac{2}{15}$$

Before you take the cumulative quiz, study this example of Martha's system. It will help you see the similarity to the traditional approach that Sue used.

<table>
<tr><td align="center">**Martha's Method**</td><td align="center">**Sue's Method**</td></tr>
</table>

$$\frac{3}{4} + \frac{2}{5} = \frac{23}{20} = 1\frac{3}{20}$$

Sue's Method:

$$+ \begin{matrix} \frac{3}{4} = ⑤ \to \frac{15}{20} \\ \frac{2}{5} = ④ \to \frac{8}{20} \end{matrix}$$

$$\frac{23}{20} = 1\frac{3}{20}$$

Denominator — $4 \times 5 = 20$
(Also 5×4)

Numerator — $3 \times 5 = 15$
$2 \times 4 = \underline{8}$
23

Denominator — $5 \times 4 = 20$
$4 \times 5 = 20$

Numerator — $3 \times 5 = 15$
$2 \times 4 = \underline{8}$
23

Rules for Reducing Fractions

1. Divide the terms of the fractions by the largest number that goes **evenly** into **both** numbers.

2. Check your answers to see if there is another number that will divide both terms. (If you have really found the largest factor, this step is unnecessary.)

Example:

$$\frac{30}{45}$$

Think, "What is the largest number that will divide both 30 and 45?"
That number is fifteen.

$$\frac{30}{45} \quad \frac{15}{15} \quad \frac{2}{3}$$

Suppose you see that 5 will divide both 30 and 45.

$$\frac{30}{45} \quad \frac{5}{5} \quad \frac{6}{9}$$

Now you need to use rule two because both 6 and 9 can be divided by 3.

$$\frac{6}{9} \quad \frac{3}{3} \quad \frac{2}{3}$$

Tips for Finding the Largest Factor

1. Try the smaller number into the larger one. This works often enough for the technique to be a good first step.

2. If both terms are even numbers, they will always divide by 2.

$$\frac{22}{66}$$

Both 22 and 66 are even numbers, so they will reduce by 2. However, both 22 and 66 can be divided by 22.

$$\frac{22}{66} \qquad \frac{22}{22} \qquad \frac{1}{3}$$

3. If the terms end in 0 and 5, they are both divisible by 5.

$$\frac{60}{75} \qquad \frac{5}{5} \qquad \frac{12}{15}$$ Not in lowest terms. Go to rule two.

$$\frac{12}{15} \qquad \frac{3}{3} \qquad \frac{4}{5}$$

4. If both terms are divisible by a number, they may also be divisible by a multiple of that number.

$$\frac{16}{24}$$

Both of these numbers are even, so 2 will divide both of them, but so will 4 and 8. Since 8 is the largest, use it.

$$\frac{16}{24} \qquad \frac{8}{8} \qquad \frac{2}{3}$$

Here's another one like that.

$$\frac{28}{42}$$

Both 28 and 42 are divisible by 7, but also 14 ($7 \times 2 = 14$). These 2 numbers have a factor that is a multiple of 7. As you can see from the comparison, Sue and Martha dealt with the same number relationships.

CUMULATIVE QUIZ (Answers on page 210.)

Refresher questions from Chapter 1:

1.
$$\begin{array}{r} \frac{2}{3} \\ + \frac{7}{8} \\ \hline \end{array}$$

2.
$$\begin{array}{r} \frac{2}{9} \\ + \frac{5}{6} \\ \hline \end{array}$$

3.
$$\begin{array}{r} \frac{3}{8} \\ - \frac{1}{7} \\ \hline \end{array}$$

Solve these problems in your head:

4.

$$\frac{2}{3} + \frac{3}{5} =$$

5.

$$\frac{2}{3} - \frac{5}{9} =$$

Complete these problems:

6. $\dfrac{\boxed{}}{3} + \dfrac{6}{\boxed{}} = \dfrac{\boxed{}}{21} = 1\frac{11}{21}$

7. $\dfrac{\boxed{}}{\boxed{}} + \dfrac{\boxed{}}{9} = \dfrac{\boxed{}}{27} = \frac{7}{9}$

Reduce these fractions:

8. A. $\dfrac{16}{48} =$ **B.** $\dfrac{18}{36} =$ **C.** $\dfrac{21}{63} =$ **D.** $\dfrac{29}{7} =$ **E.** $\dfrac{55}{10} =$

F. $\dfrac{21}{17} =$ **G.** $\dfrac{15}{75} =$ **H.** $\dfrac{24}{18} =$ **I.** $\dfrac{21}{12} =$ **J.** $\dfrac{38}{3} =$

9. Martha bought four remnants of material on sale at a department store. Here are their sizes: $2\frac{1}{3}$ yards, $3\frac{1}{2}$ yards, $4\frac{1}{4}$ yards, and $2\frac{5}{9}$ yards. How many yards of material did she buy? Answer _____ .

10. Bill wanted to lose some weight before the "big run." He went on a diet and the first week he lost $2\frac{1}{2}$ pounds. The second week he lost $3\frac{1}{4}$ pounds. The next week, though, he gained back $1\frac{1}{8}$ pounds. If he weighed $198\frac{1}{4}$ pounds when he started dieting, how much did he weigh after 3 weeks? Answer _____ .

My score on this cumulative quiz _____
(number right)

CHALLENGE

Now that you are a Sherlock Holmes of the number world, maybe you would like a real challenge. Below is an addition of fractions problem in which the numerals have been changed to shapes. Each shape stands for a numeral. Can you determine what the problem is? (Clue: Where is the identity element?) (Answers on page 211.)

$$\frac{\triangle}{\square} \; + \; \frac{\bigcirc}{\hexagon} \; = \; \frac{\bigcirc\bigcirc}{\bigcirc\triangle}$$

To get the denominator

$$\square \times \hexagon = \bigcirc\triangle$$

To get the numerator

$$\triangle \times \hexagon = \oval$$

$$\square \times \bigcirc = \square$$

$$\oval + \square = \bigcirc\bigcirc$$

STEVE WISE SAYS

1. To find the new denominator (in the General Case Statement) multiply the two denominators.

2. To find the new numerator, cross multiply one numerator by the other denominator, and add it to the other cross multiplication.

3. General Case Statement

$$\frac{A}{B} + \frac{C}{D} = \frac{(AD) + (CB)}{BD} \qquad\qquad \frac{A}{B} - \frac{C}{D} = \frac{(AD) - (CB)}{BD}$$

4. Here are Martha's models one more time.

$$\frac{1}{4} + \frac{1}{3} = \frac{7}{12}$$

$$\frac{2}{3} + \frac{1}{4} = \frac{11}{12}$$

$$\frac{2}{3} + \frac{3}{5} = \frac{19}{15}$$

$$\frac{3}{4} - \frac{2}{3} = \frac{1}{12}$$

The answers to the problems are in the problems.

CHAPTER THREE:
Unmixed Mixed Numbers

1 PREVIEW

In this segment Todd gets drawn into David's love of number theory. They talk about infinity and the infinities within it. One important discovery Todd makes is that it is often desirable to change the name of a number, but care must be taken to be certain that in changing the name the quantity stays the same.

Later Frank prepares his students to solve mixed number problems, then gives them an opportunity to share some of their experiences with mixed numbers.

Important Vocabulary

Greater Than/Less Than — In mathematics there are symbols that tell about several states of equality. The one you are most familiar with is equal (=). There is also one that means not equal (<>). Many times, especially in estimating answers, it is helpful to know < means less than. This symbol is used like this: N < 6. It is read, "N is less than 6." Or you might say N > 6, which is read, "N is greater than 6."

Infinite — This is another form of the word "infinity." It means endless.

Inverse — In this program they say it means "backward." In a way it does. In math the inverse of addition is subtraction, and the inverse of multiplication is division.

Negative Numbers — If a number is less than zero, it is called a negative number. Think of a thermometer. Temperature can be "below zero." In order to express these numbers a minus sign is used. −2 means two steps less than zero.

Number Line — This is a picture of our number system. Such a line exists only in our imagination. You must remember that number is only an idea.

Numeral — A numeral is a way of expressing the idea of number. "5" is a numeral. It expresses the idea of this quantity: ⧉.

Positive Numbers — Numbers that express a quantity more than zero are called positive numbers. Most of the computation we do is in positive numbers.

Regrouping — This term is preferred to "borrowing." It means expressing a quantity in a different way so it is more usable for the purpose of computing.

2 GOAL SETTING EXERCISE   (Answers on page 212.)

1. Locate these quantities on the line.

$1\frac{3}{4}$, $2\frac{1}{2}$, $3\frac{1}{8}$, $5\frac{7}{8}$, $3\frac{3}{5}$, $4\frac{2}{3}$, $4\frac{1}{2}$, $5\frac{1}{3}$

2. For each of the mixed numbers in number 1 (above), make a fraction family with six members.

3. Look at the following problems. Without actually figuring them out, estimate the two numbers the answer will fall between. (Try to get as close as possible.)

    A. $4\frac{1}{2} + 5\frac{3}{4}$ somewhere between _____ and _____

    B. $2\frac{1}{3} + 4\frac{7}{8}$ somewhere between _____ and _____

    C. $1\frac{1}{4} + 3\frac{1}{2}$ somewhere between _____ and _____

    D. $7\frac{1}{4} + 3\frac{1}{2}$ somewhere between _____ and _____

    E. $2\frac{1}{2} + 6\frac{1}{2}$ somewhere between _____ and _____

    F. $3\frac{1}{3} + 7\frac{7}{8}$ somewhere between _____ and _____

    G. $4\frac{1}{4} + 3\frac{1}{8}$ somewhere between _____ and _____

4. Express the following mixed numbers as improper fractions.

A. $4\frac{1}{2} =$ **B.** $6\frac{2}{3} =$ **C.** $7\frac{1}{2} =$ **D.** $2\frac{1}{4} =$

E. $7\frac{7}{8} =$ **F.** $3\frac{3}{8} =$ **G.** $5\frac{5}{9} =$ **H.** $6\frac{1}{3} =$

I. $9\frac{7}{8} =$ **J.** $10\frac{2}{3} =$ **K.** $12\frac{1}{4} =$

5. Express the following improper fractions as mixed numbers.

A. $\frac{11}{4} =$ **B.** $\frac{23}{7} =$ **C.** $\frac{46}{8} =$ **D.** $\frac{27}{3} =$

E. $\frac{9}{2} =$ **F.** $\frac{3}{1} =$

6. Add the following mixed numbers.

A. $2\frac{1}{2}$ $+ 3\frac{1}{3}$ **B.** $7\frac{1}{2}$ $+ 8\frac{2}{7}$ **C.** $9\frac{2}{5}$ $+ 2\frac{3}{8}$ **D.** $7\frac{6}{7}$ $+ 2\frac{1}{9}$

7. Subtract the following mixed numbers.

A. $4\frac{3}{4}$ $- 2\frac{1}{2}$ **B.** $7\frac{7}{8}$ $- 1\frac{3}{4}$ **C.** $2\frac{3}{8}$ $- 1\frac{1}{4}$

8. Subtract the following mixed numbers.

A. 3
   $- 2\frac{1}{2}$

B. $4\frac{1}{3}$
   $- 2\frac{3}{5}$

C. $7\frac{1}{6}$
   $- 3\frac{5}{8}$

9. If Sue canned $8\frac{3}{4}$ gallons of tomato juice one day, and $12\frac{1}{8}$ gallons the next day, how many gallons of juice did she can altogether?

10. Todd sold 87 pints of paint to an auto body shop. How many gallons is this?

GOAL PROFILE

When You Watch the Program

☐ **A.** If you got them all right, then .... Hooray!

See if you can find a short cut to the way our friends solve these problems.

☐ **B.** If you missed any part of number 1, then ....

Concentrate on what David, Todd, and Steve Wise have to say about the number line.

☐ **C.** If you missed any part of number 2, then ....

Review the Rational Families chart on pages 13 and 14.

☐ **D.** If you missed any part of number 3, then ....

Todd explains this process. Listen carefully to how he knows the size an answer is going to be.

☐ E.   If you missed any part of
number 4, then ....

This idea comes up several times in
the program. Ask yourself, "What does
the line between the terms of a fraction
mean?"

☐ F.   If you missed any part of
number 5, then ....

Pay particular attention to what
Frank and Steve Wise say about the
process of regrouping.

☐ G.   If you missed any part of
numbers 6, 7, or 8, then ..

These are regrouping problems, too.
Look back to Chapter Two to see how
you handled it there. Be especially
alert to the part of the program where
this process is discussed.

☐ H.   If you missed any part of
numbers 9 or 10, then ....

Study the key words in Chapter One on
page 1. Listen for the word clues Todd
and Bill talk about.

3 **NOW YOU ARE READY TO WATCH THE PROGRAM,
"UNMIXED MIXED NUMBERS."**

4 REACT, PRACTICE, AND EXTEND. (Answers on page 213.)

1. Here are some problems exactly as they were stated in the program. Can you solve them now?

   A. $4\frac{1}{4}$
   $+ 2\frac{3}{4}$

   B. $4\frac{3}{4}$
   $+ 2\frac{7}{8}$

   C. $5\frac{7}{8}$
   $- 2\frac{3}{8}$

   D. $4\frac{1}{4}$
   $- 2\frac{3}{4}$

2. See how many ways you can re-name this quantity.

   $4\frac{7}{8}$ (Example: $4\frac{14}{16}$; $3\frac{15}{8}$; etc.)

3. Fill in the missing numbers.

   A. $\boxed{}\frac{2}{3} = \frac{14}{3}$

   B. $3\frac{7}{\boxed{}} = \frac{43}{\boxed{}}$

   C. $\boxed{}\frac{5}{9} = \frac{41}{9}$

   D. $3\frac{7}{\boxed{}} = 5\frac{1}{3}$

   E. $2\frac{10}{\boxed{}} = 4\frac{1}{2}$

4. Vocabulary Matching. (Including some from other chapters.)

1. Identity element   ____

2. Rational number family   ____

3. Inverse operations   ____

4. Re-grouping   ____

5. Infinity   ____

6. Mixed numbers   ____

7. Improper fraction   ____

8. Numerator   ____

A. An expression of a quantity that requires a whole number and a fraction in order to name it.

B. Changing the name of a number for the purpose of computing or simplifying.

C. The number in an operation that when entered into the computation does nothing to the results.

D. What addition is to subtraction and division is to multiplication.

E. A fractional representation that expresses a quantity more than one.

F. The theoretical end to numbers.

G. The top term of a fraction.

H. A list of equivalent fractions.

My score ____ (number right)

Tips and Short Cuts

Let's take another look at the way to get answers with addition and subtraction of mixed numbers.

Step One - Get common denominator   **Step Two** - Add

$$4\frac{2}{3} \rightarrow 4\frac{2}{3} \,\, ④ \,\, 4\frac{8}{12} \qquad\qquad 4\frac{8}{12}$$
$$+2\frac{1}{4} \rightarrow 2\frac{1}{4} \,\, ③ \,\, 2\frac{3}{12} \qquad\qquad +2\frac{3}{12}$$
$$\qquad\qquad\qquad\qquad\qquad\qquad\qquad 6\frac{11}{12}$$

Step Three - Reduce to lowest terms

$$6\frac{11}{12}$$

Another method (General Case from Chapter 2).

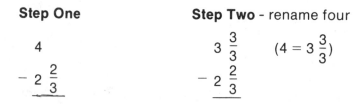

$$4 \frac{2}{3} + 2 \frac{1}{4} = 6 \frac{11}{12}$$

$$(2 \times 4) + (3 \times 1) = 11$$

Most simple mixed number problems can be solved in your head the same way that Martha learned to solve fraction problems. Remember that in a mixed number you can solve the whole number part and the fraction part separately, and then put the parts together.

Subtraction sometimes takes a little more re-grouping.

Step One

$$4$$
$$- 2 \frac{2}{3}$$

Step Two - rename four

$$3 \frac{3}{3} \qquad (4 = 3 \frac{3}{3})$$
$$- 2 \frac{2}{3}$$

Step Three - subtract

$$3 \frac{3}{3}$$
$$- 2 \frac{2}{3}$$
$$\overline{1 \frac{1}{3}}$$

Step Four - reduce whenever needed

$$1 \frac{1}{3}$$

The General Case will work for subtraction, too. However, it is probably easier to use if the mixed numbers have been changed to improper fractions first.

$$4 - 2 \frac{2}{3} = \frac{12}{3} - \frac{8}{3} = \frac{4}{3} = 1 \frac{1}{3}$$

$$(4 \times 3) - (8 \times 1) = 4$$

Even so, if the numbers are very large, it is easier to use the common denominator method because the numbers get so large that few people can keep them in their heads. The best way to use the General Case Statement is with simple problems that you can solve just by looking at them.

Example:

$$3\frac{1}{2} + 2\frac{1}{3} = 5\frac{5}{6}$$

$$7\frac{7}{8} + 9\frac{9}{16}$$

Easy to work by
General Case

Tough to work by General Case,
but easy with common denominator approach.

In order to use the above system effectively you need an easy way to change mixed numbers to improper fractions.

To change $5\frac{3}{7}$ to an improper fraction you ask yourself, "How many 7ths are in 5?"

You think, "$\frac{7}{7} = 1$, so $5 = \frac{7}{7} + \frac{7}{7} + \frac{7}{7} + \frac{7}{7} + \frac{7}{7} = \frac{35}{7}$.

Then add the $\frac{3}{7}$ to get $\frac{38}{7}$ . . . . $5\frac{3}{7} = \frac{38}{7}$."

But there is a short cut.

To get the $\frac{35}{7}$ you really multiplied the numerator of 7 times 5 ($5 \times 7 = 35$). Since 1 expressed as sevenths is $\frac{7}{7}$, the 5 doesn't care **which** seven you multiply by to get the 35.

In the case of $5\frac{3}{7}$, you say, "$5 \times 7 = 35$. $35 + 3 = 38$."

$$5\frac{3}{7}\begin{array}{c}+\\\uparrow\\\rightarrow\end{array}\begin{array}{c}\rightarrow\\=\\\end{array}\frac{38}{7}$$

$5 \times 7 + 3 = 38$ (7 is still the denominator)

Got it? You'll have a chance later on to refine your skill in this important process.

The reverse of this process is the way you can change an improper fraction to a mixed number.

$$\frac{19}{8} = 8\overline{)19}^{2} = 2\frac{3}{8}$$
$$\phantom{\frac{19}{8} = 8)}\underline{16}$$
$$\phantom{\frac{19}{8} = 8)}3$$

REMEMBERING THE THINGS TO REMEMBER

- Mixed numbers are most often expressed as a whole number and a fraction.
- Mixed numbers fall on the number line somewhere between the whole numbers.
- An "improper fraction" has a numerator larger than the denominator.
- Improper fractions in their simplest forms are mixed numbers.
- Mixed numbers can be written in an infinite number of ways.
- The line between the terms of a fraction means "divided by."

CUMULATIVE QUIZ (Answers on page 213.)

From Chapter One:

1.
A. $\dfrac{5}{7}$ $+\dfrac{7}{8}$

B. $\dfrac{6}{11}$ $+\dfrac{3}{22}$

C. $\dfrac{9}{14}$ $+\dfrac{2}{7}$

D. $\dfrac{2}{3}$ $-\dfrac{5}{8}$

E. $\dfrac{3}{8}$ $-\dfrac{1}{7}$

F. $\dfrac{7}{8}$ $-\dfrac{2}{9}$

From Chapter Two, solve these in your head:

2.
A. $\dfrac{2}{3} + \dfrac{1}{4} =$

B. $\dfrac{3}{8} + \dfrac{1}{5} =$

C. $\dfrac{4}{5} + \dfrac{1}{8} =$

D. $\dfrac{3}{4} + \dfrac{5}{8} =$

E. $\dfrac{4}{9} + \dfrac{7}{8} =$

F. $\dfrac{2}{7} + \dfrac{2}{9} =$

From Chapter Three

3. Add and reduce all answers to lowest terms.

A. $4\dfrac{2}{3}$ $+ 3\dfrac{1}{2}$

B. $3\dfrac{1}{3}$ $+ 2\dfrac{7}{8}$

C. $7\dfrac{3}{4}$ $+ 1\dfrac{5}{9}$

D. $36\dfrac{4}{5}$ $+ 22\dfrac{7}{8}$

E. $26\dfrac{4}{9}$ $+ 3\dfrac{6}{7}$

F. $3\dfrac{5}{8}$ $+ 2\dfrac{3}{4}$

G. $7\dfrac{2}{3}$ $+ 5\dfrac{1}{2}$

H. $3\dfrac{7}{8}$ $+ 2\dfrac{5}{8}$

4. Change these mixed numbers to improper fractions.

A. $4\frac{2}{3}$ **B.** $3\frac{1}{2}$ **C.** $2\frac{7}{8}$ **D.** $6\frac{5}{8}$

E. $3\frac{2}{7}$ **F.** $7\frac{1}{3}$ **G.** $16\frac{1}{4}$ **H.** $5\frac{2}{9}$

I. $4\frac{3}{10}$ **J.** $2\frac{7}{11}$

5. Change these improper fractions to mixed numbers.

A. $\frac{11}{3}$ **B.** $\frac{24}{9}$ **C.** $\frac{6}{2}$ **D.** $\frac{7}{5}$

E. $\frac{27}{9}$ **F.** $\frac{54}{13}$ **G.** $\frac{28}{8}$ **H.** $\frac{25}{4}$

I. $\frac{22}{4}$ **J.** $\frac{22}{6}$

6. Subtract these mixed numbers.

A. $4\frac{4}{5} - 2\frac{2}{5}$ **B.** $3 - 1\frac{1}{3}$ **C.** $5\frac{2}{5} - 1\frac{4}{9}$ **D.** $6\frac{1}{2} - 2\frac{3}{4}$

E. $7\frac{1}{3} - 6\frac{3}{4}$ **F.** $2\frac{1}{8} - \frac{9}{10}$ **G.** $24\frac{1}{16} - 3\frac{5}{8}$ **H.** $14\frac{1}{5} - 2\frac{3}{8}$

7. Find a mixed number that when $2\frac{1}{3}$ is subtracted from it, $3\frac{1}{2}$ remains.

8. Sue wants to put a decorative border around her bathroom. The longest side of the room is $8\frac{1}{2}$ feet. The two end walls are $6\frac{3}{4}$ feet each. The fourth wall is the shortest of all because of a door and a mirror and has only $1\frac{1}{4}$ feet of space to cover. How much border does Sue need?

9. At a church bazaar, Martha is in charge of cutting the pies. They are expecting to sell 350 pieces of pie. Each pie is cut into sixths. How many pies will be needed?

10. Bill has a 4 by 8 piece of plywood. A project he is working on calls for two pieces of plywood $\frac{3}{4}$ foot wide and 8 feet long. He also needs two pieces $1\frac{1}{2}$ feet wide and 4 feet long. What is the size of the piece that is left after he has cut the pieces he needs from the full sheet? (Be careful with this one. You may want to draw a picture.)

11. Todd is painting some signs for the store where he works. It takes $2\frac{1}{2}$ pints for the small signs and $3\frac{3}{4}$ pints of paint for the large ones. If he paints three small ones and two large ones, how much paint will he need?

12. In the problem above, if Todd started with two gallons of paint, will he have enough? Explain.

My cumulative quiz score is _____ (number right).

EXTENDING YOUR UNDERSTANDING

Bill has a favorite jogging course that usually takes him an hour and a half to run. Once in awhile, though, he can run the course in only ninety minutes. How can you explain this? (Answers on page 216.)

Oh, by the way, if a hen and a half can lay an egg and a half in a day and a half, how long would it take six chickens to lay a dozen eggs? (Sorry, the answer to this one is given only in the video program.)

STEVE WISE SAYS

1. Mixed numbers are most often expressed as a whole number and a fraction as in $4\frac{3}{4}$ and $4\frac{5}{8}$, or any equivalent combination of numbers. They fall on the number line between the whole numbers.

2. For each pair of whole numbers, there are uncountable mixed numbers that fall between them.

3. Any point on the number line can have several different names. In fact, it can have an unlimited number of names.

4. The line between the numerator and the denominator means to divide.

5. In regrouping you express a new whole number and a fraction. For example: $\quad 4\frac{1}{4} + 1\frac{3}{4} = 5\frac{4}{4} \qquad \frac{4}{4} = 1$

    $$\text{therefore } 5\frac{4}{4} = 6$$

6. Subtraction, the inverse of addition, sometimes requires you to do the opposite.

    $$6 - 1\frac{3}{4} = 5\frac{4}{4} - 1\frac{3}{4} = 4\frac{1}{4}$$

7. When you change a whole number to a mixed number, you aren't changing value, just the name.

8. Be sure when you say one expression equals another that it really does.

CHAPTER FOUR:
Show and Tell

1 PREVIEW

In this program our friends look at most of the ideas that have been investigated in the three previous scripts. They seem to be having a lot of fun doing it, too. Even though this is mainly review, be alert to some new things sneaking in.

It might be a good idea to take the advice of the students as they good-naturedly go over the processes involved in addition and subtraction of fractions and mixed numbers "one more time."

Part of what they are doing is preparing the way to go on to the next program. They want to be sure none of us has missed anything.

Important Vocabulary

Before you watch the TV program it would be a good idea to review the words from the previous chapters.

New Vocabulary:

Circumference — This is the distance around the circle.

Compass — As it is used in this program, it is an instrument used to draw circles.

Diameter — This is the distance across a circle measured through the center.

Pi — The ratio of the circumference to the diameter of a circle is given the name of this Greek letter. This relationship is the same for all circles, no matter how large or small.

2 GOAL SETTING EXERCISE (Answers on page 217.)

1. Count from 0 to 1 by 16ths. (All fractions expressed in lowest terms.)

2. In these circles, express the following fraction representations.

$$\frac{4}{5} \quad \frac{7}{9} \quad \frac{3}{12} \quad \frac{5}{15}$$

3. This illustration might be called a "sharing picture." $\dfrac{\bigstar\bigstar}{\bigstar\bigstar\bigstar\bigstar\bigstar\bigstar}$

It's much like telling about 2 books shared by 6 people. Draw a "sharing picture" for the rest of these examples.

A. $\dfrac{3}{7} =$ **B.** $\dfrac{4}{5} =$ **C.** $\dfrac{7}{9} =$

D. $\dfrac{2}{5} =$ **E.** $\dfrac{3}{16} =$ **F.** $\dfrac{3}{9} =$

G. $\dfrac{5}{10} =$ **H.** $\dfrac{8}{12} =$

4. The last three examples in number 3 (above) can have a simpler rate of sharing expressed. Draw a "sharing picture" of these that show their simplest rate of sharing.

A. $\dfrac{3}{9} =$ **B.** $\dfrac{5}{10} =$ **C.** $\dfrac{8}{12} =$

5. Once more, fraction families. Below are some fractions. They are representatives of three families. Sort them out and put them in their proper family and order. Not all the members are here so the families won't be complete.

$$\frac{8}{12}, \quad \frac{14}{21}, \quad \frac{15}{25}, \quad \frac{30}{48}, \quad \frac{6}{10}, \quad \frac{16}{24}, \quad \frac{9}{15}, \quad \frac{12}{18}, \quad \frac{35}{56}, \quad \frac{6}{9}, \quad \frac{12}{20}, \quad \frac{20}{32}, \quad \frac{10}{16}, \quad \frac{21}{35}, \quad \frac{10}{15}$$

A.

B.

C.

6. What mixed number plus $1\frac{1}{3}$ is $7\frac{1}{2}$ more than $4\frac{1}{5}$?

7. **A.** Express 9 oz. as a fraction of a pound.

   B. Express 3 pt. as a fraction of a gallon.

   C. Express 7 in. as a fraction of a foot.

   D. Express 22 in. as a fraction of a yard.

8. Here are two problems that are "solved" incorrectly. Find the errors and correct them.

   A.
   $$4\frac{1}{3} = 4\frac{5}{15}$$
   $$-\ 2\frac{4}{5} = 2\frac{4}{15}$$
   $$\overline{2\frac{1}{15}}$$

   B.
   $$6\frac{1}{3} = 6\frac{2}{6} = 6\frac{8}{6}$$
   $$-\ 2\frac{1}{2} = 2\frac{3}{6} = 2\frac{3}{6}$$
   $$\overline{4\frac{5}{6}}$$

GOAL PROFILE

Put a check mark in the box that fits your situation.

When You Watch the Program

☐ A. If you got them all right —
     pick up your hero medal.

Even though you seem to know all of the ideas in the first four programs, Frank demonstrates a different way of looking at the members of a fraction family. This becomes very important later on. Pay close attention to this portion.

☐ B. If you missed any part of
     number 1, then . . . .

Review the fraction family chart on pages 13 & 14, and be alert when Bill talks about the ideas of a rational family.

☐ C. If you missed any part of
     number 2, then . . . .

Review page 4 of Chapter One, then when you watch the program, look for clues in what Martha and Todd are saying.

☐ D. If you missed any part of
     number 3, then . . . .

Steve Wise will give you the clues you need. Listen carefully.

☐ E. If you missed any part of
     number 4, then . . . .

You are still having trouble with reducing. Sue and Bill will help you in this program.

☐ F. If you missed any part of
     number 5, then . . . .

This is a reducing exercise also. Pay very close attention to those parts of the program that refer to changing fractions to their lowest terms.

☐ G. If you missed any part of
      number 6, then ....
                                    Review Chapter Three on adding and
                                    subtracting mixed numbers. Then be
                                    particularly attentive to what Martha
                                    says about adding and subtracting
                                    mixed numbers.

☐ H. If you missed any part of
      number 7, then ....
                                    Steve Wise has some advice and
                                    information. Sue will give you some
                                    clues, too.

☐ I. If you missed any part of
      number 8, then ....
                                    Review Chapter Three. Listen carefully
                                    as Sue solves Bill's pipe problem. Martha
                                    can help you, too.

3 NOW YOU ARE READY TO WATCH THE PROGRAM, "SHOW AND TELL"

4 **REACT, PRACTICE, AND EXTEND.** (Answers on page 218.)

Tips and Short Cuts

Before you start with the practice section, let's go over once again the new fraction family relationship Frank pointed out to the students.

First take any two members of the same fraction family.

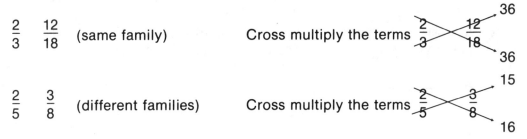

$\frac{2}{3}$ $\frac{12}{18}$ (same family)   Cross multiply the terms

$\frac{2}{5}$ $\frac{3}{8}$ (different families)   Cross multiply the terms

If they are in the same family, the products will be the same. This idea will become more important as time goes on.

Something Bill said is important, too. "Mixed numbers fit the fraction family pattern, too."

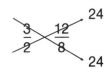

This system gives you a tool to quickly determine if two fractions are in the same family.

Remember, at any space between numbers there is an infinite number of other numbers — as many numbers as there are altogether.

1. Draw lines in these shapes to express the following fractions.

A. $\frac{3}{6}$ shaded, $\frac{3}{6}$ unshaded

B. $\frac{6}{8}$ shaded, $\frac{2}{8}$ unshaded

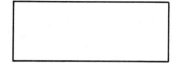

C. $\frac{9}{12}$ shaded, $\frac{3}{12}$ unshaded

2. In exercise number one above, what simpler names could you give to each of the unshaded portions?

    A. _____   **B.** _____   **C.** _____

3. Draw pie-like illustrations to show the following improper fractions.

    Example: $\frac{3}{2}$

    A. $\frac{26}{6}$ **B.** $\frac{32}{5}$ **C.** $\frac{10}{4}$

4. Using Frank's cross-multiplying technique, which of the following sets of fractions are members of the same family? Circle the examples that are in the same family.

    A. $\frac{2}{3}$ and $\frac{8}{12}$ **B.** $\frac{3}{4}$ and $\frac{10}{15}$ **C.** $\frac{2}{5}$ and $\frac{8}{20}$

    D. $\frac{10}{15}$ and $\frac{12}{18}$ **E.** $\frac{14}{42}$ and $\frac{7}{21}$ **F.** $4\frac{1}{3}$ and $3\frac{16}{12}$

5. Martha used a system of breaking up the whole numbers and the fractions to get mixed number answers. Show how you'd break up these examples and then put them back together again.

A.
$$+\quad\begin{array}{r} 4\frac{1}{3} \\ 5\frac{1}{2} \end{array}$$

B.
$$+\quad\begin{array}{r} 7\frac{1}{2} \\ 2\frac{1}{4} \\ 3\frac{3}{8} \end{array}$$

C.
$$-\quad\begin{array}{r} 4\frac{7}{8} \\ 3\frac{5}{12} \end{array}$$

6. David came to the class to talk about Pi (π). According to him such mathematical formulas are nothing to get excited about. In the case of Pi, it's just a specialized mixed number. They did discover that the peculiar relationship of circumference to diameter is the improper fraction of $\frac{22}{7}$. Make a fraction family of ten members starting with $\frac{22}{7}$. ($\frac{22}{7}$ and other expressions of Pi are approximations, but they compute circles as accurately as we can measure them.)

7. Make a number line with the above family. Use the divisions indicated to record them, then answer the questions about them.

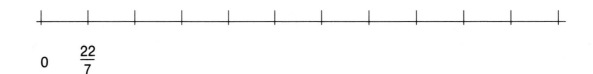

0     $\frac{22}{7}$

A. By looking at your number line, fill in the missing numbers.

If the diameter is . . .	The circumference is . . .
7	22
___	110
49	___
35	___
___	44
___	66
63	___
___	88

B. Now do some estimating.

If the diameter is . . .	The circumference is between . . .
9	22 & 44
26	___ & ___
51	___ & ___
36	___ & ___
12	___ & ___

VOCABULARY FILL-IN-THE-BLANK (Answers on page 219.)

Since this is the last program dealing directly with addition and subtraction of fractions, you will not be hearing these words as often. Below are the definitions for the important words in the first four chapters. All you have to do is write in the word or term being defined.

1. The end of numbers _____

2. The top term of a fraction _____

3. A fraction and a whole number used together to tell

   the size of a number _____

4. What addition is to subtraction and

   division is to multiplication _____

   _____

5. The bottom term of a fraction _____

6. A list of equal fractions _____

7. A fraction whose terms have a common factor of

   only 1 is said to be in _____

8. A picture of the number system _____

   _____

9. In multiplication, the number 1 _____

   _____

10. When the denominators of two fractions are
    the same, the fractions are said to have a

    _____

CUMULATIVE QUIZ (Answers on page 220.)

From Chapter One:

1. A. $\dfrac{2}{9}$ B. $\dfrac{5}{7}$ C. $\dfrac{6}{11}$ D. $\dfrac{9}{14}$
   $+\dfrac{5}{6}$ $+\dfrac{7}{8}$ $+\dfrac{3}{22}$ $+\dfrac{2}{7}$

   E. $\dfrac{2}{3}$ F. $\dfrac{3}{8}$ G. $\dfrac{7}{9}$ H. $\dfrac{5}{12}$
   $-\dfrac{5}{8}$ $-\dfrac{1}{7}$ $-\dfrac{1}{3}$ $-\dfrac{1}{6}$

From Chapter Two:

2. Reduce these fractions to their lowest terms.

   A. $\dfrac{16}{48} =$ B. $\dfrac{18}{36} =$ C. $\dfrac{21}{63} =$ D. $\dfrac{29}{7} =$

   E. $\dfrac{55}{10} =$ F. $\dfrac{21}{7} =$ G. $\dfrac{38}{3} =$

From Chapter Three:

3. Add these mixed numbers. Always reduce to lowest terms.

   A. $4\dfrac{2}{3}$ B. $3\dfrac{1}{3}$ C. $7\dfrac{3}{4}$ D. $36\dfrac{4}{5}$ E. $26\dfrac{4}{9}$
   $+3\dfrac{1}{2}$ $+2\dfrac{7}{8}$ $+1\dfrac{5}{9}$ $+22\dfrac{7}{8}$ $+3\dfrac{6}{7}$

4. Change these mixed numbers to improper fractions.

   A. $5\dfrac{6}{7} =$ B. $3\dfrac{3}{7} =$ C. $2\dfrac{2}{9} =$ D. $5\dfrac{7}{8} =$

E. $6\frac{3}{4} =$ **F.** $17 =$ **G.** $24\frac{1}{6} =$ **H.** $15\frac{1}{3} =$

I. $16\frac{1}{8} =$ **J.** $14\frac{1}{2} =$

5. Subtract these mixed numbers.

A. 7 **B.** $8\frac{4}{5}$ **C.** $6\frac{1}{3}$ **D.** $9\frac{7}{8}$

$-3\frac{1}{7}$ $-2\frac{1}{3}$ $-2\frac{5}{8}$ $-2\frac{15}{16}$

6. Supply the missing numbers.

A.

$2\dfrac{\boxed{}}{3} = 1\dfrac{\boxed{}}{15}$

$-1\dfrac{3}{\boxed{}} = 1\dfrac{\boxed{}}{\boxed{}}$

$\dfrac{\overline{}}{11}$

$\boxed{}$

B.

$3\dfrac{\boxed{}}{8} = 3\dfrac{\boxed{}}{8} = 2\dfrac{\boxed{}}{8}$

$-1\dfrac{\boxed{}}{\boxed{}} = 1\dfrac{\boxed{}}{8} = 1\dfrac{\boxed{}}{8}$

$1\dfrac{3}{8}$

7. What number plus $\frac{1}{3}$ is $\frac{5}{6}$ more than $\frac{1}{2}$?

8. Todd said he had a box with 12 paint cans in it and half of them were pints. Of the rest, some were quarts, some were half gallons, and some were gallons. If the cans totaled exactly 5 gallons, how many of each size were in the box?

9. Sue is $4\frac{1}{2}$ years older than her sister. Her sister is $1\frac{1}{2}$ years younger than their brother. Their brother is 30. How old is Sue? Her sister?

10. If there are 26 people in a room and 15 of them are women, what is the fractional part that are women? Men?

11. The public library is $4\frac{1}{2}$ blocks from the adult school. David walked there and back 4 times last week. If there are 12 blocks in a mile, how many miles did David walk just to get to the library and back?

Cumulative quiz score _____ (number right)

EXTENDING YOUR UNDERSTANDING (Answers on page 221.)

Here are some fraction problems with the signs omitted. By inserting plus and minus signs between the numbers, can you get the answer indicated?

1. **A.** $\frac{1}{2}\ \frac{2}{3}\ \frac{3}{4} = 1\frac{11}{12}$ **B.** $\frac{1}{2}\ \frac{2}{3}\ \frac{3}{4} = \frac{5}{12}$ **C.** $\frac{1}{2}\ \frac{2}{3}\ \frac{3}{4} = \frac{7}{12}$

2. Is it possible to have a fraction that looks like this?

$$\frac{3\frac{1}{2}}{4}$$

3. If it is possible, what would the next number of this family be?

STEVE WISE SAYS:

1. Fractions and mixed numbers are part of a family of equal fractions.

2. It might be a good idea for you to take Martha's advice, "Practice, practice, practice."

3. The formula for finding the circumference is the circumference equals Pi times the diameter ($C = \pi D$).

4. Don't let formulas bother you. The only purpose they serve is to give you a simple way to remember how to calculate different problems.

5. π is **just a mixed number.**

CHAPTER FIVE:
Operating Room

1 **PREVIEW**

Now our friends move into the area of multiplication and division of fractions. In "Operating Room" you'll get considerable "operating room" to deal with the most mystifying part of the arithmetic of fractions. The purpose of this program is to demonstrate the similarities of multiplication and division of fractions and what you already know about operating with whole numbers.

This program takes a different approach to computing. Frank gives the students a set of rules. If followed, the rules will be sufficient to solve any problems you are likely to encounter. However, as both Frank and David point out, unless the rules are understood, people forget.

When you have finished this program, you will be able to multiply and divide fractions and mixed numbers with the best of them. In this program and the next, steps will be taken to keep you from forgetting.

In the third section the students offer some examples in their experience that show the difficulties of using these new skills in the everyday world. As they point out, problems we come across every day don't have nice neat answers. You often need to use other tools besides pure rules.

Important Vocabulary

Additive Quality — Multiplication is sometimes thought of as a series of additions. If it is this, then division, the inverse, is in the same way a series of subtractions.

Dividend — In a division problem, the number to be divided is the dividend.

Divisor — The number "divided by" is the divisor. This is the number of "piles" the dividend is to be re-grouped into to get the answer. Another important idea is that the order of the divisor and the dividend **DOES** make a difference ($8 \div 4 \neq 4 \div 8$).

Inverse Operations — We've had this word before, but now it is of vital importance. It means the "backwards" of another operation. In this program multiplication and division are said to be inverse operations. You will see many examples of how this works and why it is so important. Don't confuse this term with "invert."

Invert — In this program you will hear the rule for division of fractions stated as, "Invert the divisor and follow the rules for multiplication." It means to turn the divisor upside down.

Multiplicand — In a multiplication problem, the number that is being multiplied.

Multiplier — The number being multiplied by is the multiplier. It is important to know that in multiplication, the order of the multiplier and the multiplicand is unimportant ($3 \times 4 = 4 \times 3$).

Product — This is the name given to the answer in a multiplication problem.

Quotient — This is the name for the answer of a division problem.

2 GOAL SETTING EXERCISE (Answers on page 222.)

1. Multiply these examples (reduce answers).

   A. $\frac{1}{2} \times \frac{1}{3} =$ **B.** $\frac{2}{3} \times \frac{3}{4} =$

   C. $\frac{5}{8} \times \frac{2}{7} =$ **D.** $\frac{4}{5} \times \frac{4}{9} =$

2. Multiply these fractions times whole numbers (reduce answers to simplest form).

   A. $4 \times \frac{5}{8} =$ **B.** $\frac{3}{4} \times 6 =$

   C. $7 \times \frac{1}{2} =$ **D.** $8 \times \frac{5}{8} =$

3. Multiply these fractions times mixed numbers.

   A. $3\frac{1}{3} \times \frac{1}{2} =$

   B. $2\frac{2}{3} \times \frac{3}{8} =$

   C. $5\frac{1}{7} \times \frac{3}{4} =$

   D. $3\frac{1}{2} \times \frac{5}{6} =$

4. Multiply these mixed numbers times mixed numbers.

   A. $2\frac{1}{2} \times 2\frac{1}{2} =$

   B. $6\frac{1}{4} \times 1\frac{1}{3} =$

   C. $8\frac{1}{2} \times 2\frac{2}{3} =$

   D. $9\frac{1}{3} \times 1\frac{1}{4} =$

5. Divide these examples.

   A. $14 \div \frac{1}{2} =$ **B.** $12 \div \frac{1}{3} =$

   C. $5 \div \frac{1}{2} =$ **D.** $20 \div \frac{1}{3} =$

6. **A.** $1\frac{1}{3} \div \frac{3}{4} =$ **B.** $2\frac{1}{4} \div \frac{1}{8} =$

   C. $2\frac{1}{6} \div 1\frac{1}{4} =$ **D.** $3\frac{1}{2} \div 2\frac{1}{5} =$

7. There are 36 people in a room, and $\frac{2}{3}$ of them are women. How many women are in the room?

8. There was $\frac{7}{8}$ of a pie on the table. Todd gave half of it to Bill. How much of the total pie did he give Bill?

9. David ordered $7\frac{1}{2}$ tons of gravel for his drive. $\frac{2}{3}$ of it came in the first truck, and the rest came in a second one. How many tons were in the first truck? How many tons were in the second truck?

10. Sue was filling her gas tank at a self-service filling station. She knew her tank was almost empty. After she had put 14 gallons in the tank, the gauge read $\frac{3}{4}$ full. How many gallons would her tank hold if it were completely full?

GOAL PROFILE

Put a check mark in the box that fits your situation.

When You Watch the Program

☐   A.   If you got them all right, you're some kind of genius.

Still, learn as much as you can about inverse operations. It will make future lessons easier.

☐   B.   If you missed any part of number 1, then . . . .

Pay close attention as Frank explains rule one for the multiplication of fractions.

☐   C.   If you missed any part of number 2, then . . . .

You'll need to be certain you understand rule number 2, which tells you about multiplying fractions and whole numbers.

☐   D.   If you missed any part of numbers 3 or 4, then . . . .

Review Chapter Three page 37, which talks about converting mixed numbers to improper fractions. Listen as the students discover the rule for multiplying mixed numbers.

☐ E. If you missed any part of
        number 5, then ....

Pay particular attention to David
and Frank as they explain what it
means to divide fractions.

☐ F. If you missed any part of
        number 6, then ....

Review Chapter Three page 37. Learn
more about converting mixed numbers
to improper fractions. Memorize the
rule for division of fractions.

☐ G. If you missed any part of
        number 7, then ....

You'll need to watch very closely as
the students share their "real life"
experiences.

☐ H. If you missed number 8 or
        9, then ....

The secret is in the program a couple
of times. What does the word "of" tell
you to do when dealing with fractions?

☐ I. If you missed number 10,
        then ....

David and Frank talk about this idea.
The question Frank asks is, "Should
we show the inverse here?"

3 NOW YOU ARE READY TO WATCH THE PROGRAM, "OPERATING ROOM."

4 REACT, PRACTICE, AND EXTEND.

Tips and Short Cuts

Here are the rules for multiplication and division of fractions as they were listed on Frank's handout.

MULTIPLICATION OF FRACTIONS

Rule 1: To multiply fractions, multiply numerators times numerators, and denominators times denominators.

Example: $\dfrac{2}{3} \times \dfrac{1}{2} = \dfrac{2}{6} = \dfrac{1}{3}$

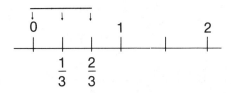

Rule 2: To multiply a whole number by a fraction, express the whole number as a fraction and follow rule 1. To express a whole number as a fraction, simply write the number over "1."

Example: $4 \times \dfrac{2}{3} = \dfrac{4}{1} \times \dfrac{2}{3} = \dfrac{8}{3} = 2\dfrac{2}{3}$

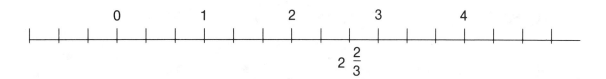

Rule 3: To multiply a mixed number times a fraction, express the mixed number as an improper fraction and follow rule 1.

Example: $1\dfrac{1}{2} \times \dfrac{1}{8} = \dfrac{3}{2} \times \dfrac{1}{8} = \dfrac{3}{16}$

$\left(\text{Think } 1\dfrac{1}{2} \times \dfrac{1}{8}\right)$

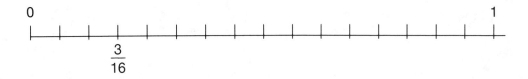

Rule 4: To multiply a mixed number times a mixed number, express both mixed numbers as improper fractions and follow rule 1.

Example:
$$2\frac{1}{5} \times 1\frac{1}{8} = \frac{11}{5} \times \frac{9}{8} = \frac{99}{40} = 2\frac{19}{40}$$

Note: A number line could be drawn to show this problem, but it is so complex it loses meaning. One of the great things about math is you can figure things you can't draw.

DIVISION OF FRACTIONS

To divide by a fraction:

Rule 1: To divide by a fraction, invert the divisor and follow the rule for multiplication of fractions.

Example:
$$\frac{3}{4} \div \frac{2}{3}$$

$$\underset{\text{dividend}}{\frac{3}{4}} \div \underset{\text{divisor}}{\frac{2}{3}} = \frac{3}{4} \times \frac{3}{2} = \frac{9}{8} = 1\frac{1}{8}$$

All the other information you might need is the same as procedures used in multiplication of fractions. Whole numbers should be changed to fractions and mixed numbers should be changed to improper fractions before they are divided.

REMEMBERING THE THINGS TO REMEMBER

To change a mixed number to a fraction, multiply the denominator of the fraction times the whole number, and then add the numerator. This gives the new numerator. The denominator stays the same. (Fuller explanation is in Chapter Four.)

Example:
$$3\frac{4}{5} = \frac{5 \times 3 + 4}{5} = \frac{19}{5}$$

$$\text{Think} \quad 3 \overset{+}{\underset{\times}{\overrightarrow{}}} \frac{4}{5}$$

IMPORTANT!

In solving word problems, the word "of" means to multiply. In the question, "What is $\frac{1}{2}$ of 8?" the "of" means to multiply ($\frac{1}{2} \times 8$).

PRACTICE:
Multiply these examples (reduce when possible). (Answers on page 222.)

1. A. $\frac{1}{2} \times \frac{1}{3} =$ B. $\frac{1}{4} \times \frac{7}{8} =$ C. $\frac{2}{3} \times \frac{3}{4} =$

   D. $\frac{7}{8} \times \frac{3}{4} =$ E. $\frac{4}{5} \times \frac{1}{2} =$ F. $\frac{6}{7} \times \frac{4}{9} =$

2. A. $2 \times \frac{3}{4} =$ B. $\frac{4}{5} \times 3 =$ C. $5 \times \frac{4}{5} =$

   D. $\frac{1}{7} \times 5 =$ E. $\frac{2}{7} \times 9 =$ F. $3 \times \frac{5}{6} =$

3. A. $2\frac{1}{3} \times \frac{7}{8} =$ B. $2\frac{5}{8} \times \frac{1}{3} =$

   C. $4\frac{1}{5} \times \frac{1}{25} =$ D. $3\frac{1}{9} \times \frac{1}{5} =$

   E. $6\frac{1}{4} \times \frac{1}{16} =$ F. $7\frac{1}{8} \times \frac{1}{8} =$

4. A. $2\frac{1}{3} \times 2\frac{1}{4} =$ B. $4 \times 2\frac{3}{8} =$

   C. $3\frac{1}{6} \times 2\frac{1}{4} =$

Divide these examples.

5. A. $\frac{6}{7} \div \frac{2}{3} =$ B. $\frac{7}{8} \div \frac{1}{4} =$ C. $\frac{3}{5} \div \frac{3}{8} =$

6. A. $2 \div \frac{1}{4} =$ B. $3\frac{1}{3} \div \frac{4}{5} =$ C. $9\frac{1}{3} \div 2\frac{1}{5} =$

7. Half of what number is $\frac{1}{3}$ of 10?

VOCABULARY STUDY (Answers on page 223.)

Most of the words in this section have to do with the names of the parts of the problems in multiplication and division. In these examples below, write in the name for the term in the problems.

_____ times the multiplier = the _____

_____ divided by the _____ = the quotient

One-half of the _____ = the _____

The quotient times the _____ = the dividend.

The product divided by the multiplicand = the _____ .

CUMULATIVE QUIZ (Answers on page 223.)

1. Add these examples (always reduce when possible).

   A. $\frac{2}{3} + \frac{1}{5} =$ B. $\frac{3}{8} + \frac{4}{5} =$ C. $2\frac{1}{3} + \frac{1}{7} =$

2. Subtract these examples.

   A. $\frac{3}{4} - \frac{1}{3} =$ B. $\frac{7}{8} - \frac{4}{5} =$ C. $2\frac{3}{5} - \frac{1}{4} =$

3. Multiply these examples.

   A. $\frac{2}{3} \times \frac{3}{8} =$ B. $4 \times \frac{2}{5} =$ C. $5\frac{1}{3} \times 2\frac{1}{2} =$

4. Divide these examples.

   A. $7 \div \frac{2}{3} =$ B. $12\frac{1}{3} \div \frac{1}{5} =$ C. $\frac{1}{5} \div 12\frac{1}{3} =$

WORD PROBLEMS (Answers on page 224.)

1. Sue said that $\frac{1}{2}$ of her time on her new job is involved in filing reports. $\frac{1}{4}$ of her time is used in making phone calls. The rest of the time she serves as a receptionist. If she works 40 hours a week, how many hours is she the receptionist?

2. How many $\frac{1}{2}$'s are there in 48?

3. Sue was working on her household budget. She found that $\frac{3}{8}$ of the money she made would be needed that month to buy new clothes for the family. If she planned to spend $120.00 for clothes, how much money did she have for all her expenses?

4. Martha and her neighbors operate a neighborhood co-op. They bought a 12-pound carton of pepper. The pepper was packaged in $\frac{1}{8}$-pound cans. How many cans were in the carton?

5. After Todd figured out the hen and egg problem, he went to the store and bought $4\frac{1}{2}$ dozen eggs for 96¢ a dozen. How much did he have to pay for them?

6. Martha lives $3\frac{1}{4}$ miles from the adult school. Sue lives $\frac{1}{3}$ as far. Todd lives 2 times as far as Martha, and Bill lives $\frac{3}{4}$ as far as Todd. How far do Sue, Todd, and Bill live from the school?

7. Sue bought 24 yards of material to make costumes for a play her daughter was to be in at school. If each costume required $3\frac{1}{2}$ yards of material, how many costumes could she make from the material?

8. The students in Frank's class decided to make some ice cream to bring to class one night. The freezer they used held 10 quarts, but when they opened it up they found that it was only $\frac{3}{4}$ full. How much ice cream had they made?

Cumulative quiz score ＿＿＿＿＿ (number right)

EXTENDING YOUR SKILLS (Answers on page 224.)

In the early chapters we talked a great deal about number lines. How does this idea relate to multiplication of fractions?

Here is a number line that shows the multiplication of whole numbers.

	2×0	2×1	2×2	2×3	2×4	2×5	2×6	2×7
	↓	↓	↓	↓	↓	↓	↓	↓
Times 2	0 1	2 3	4 5	6 7	8 9	10 11	12 13	14

This number line shows multiplication of $\frac{1}{2}$.

	$0 \times \frac{1}{2}$	$1 \times \frac{1}{2}$	$2 \times \frac{1}{2}$	$3 \times \frac{1}{2}$	$4 \times \frac{1}{2}$	$5 \times \frac{1}{2}$	$6 \times \frac{1}{2}$	$7 \times \frac{1}{2}$	$8 \times \frac{1}{2}$	$9 \times \frac{1}{2}$	$10 \times \frac{1}{2}$	$11 \times \frac{1}{2}$	$12 \times \frac{1}{2}$
	↓		↓		↓		↓		↓		↓		↓
Times $\frac{1}{2}$	0		1		2		3		4		5		6

See if you can complete the number line for the following multiplication situations. Draw in the lines and arrows to indicate multiplication of $\frac{2}{3}$ and $\frac{1}{2}$ for A and B.

1. Question — What is $4 \frac{1}{2} \times \frac{2}{3}$?

_____

Times $\frac{2}{3}$	0	1	2	3	4	5	6

2. Question — What is $5\frac{1}{3} \times \frac{3}{4}$?

_____

Times   0   1   2   3   4   5
$\frac{3}{4}$ _____

We talked about fraction families a lot. Fill in the blanks for these fractions.

3. $\dfrac{3\frac{1}{3}}{5}$ = _____ = _____

4. $\dfrac{2\frac{1}{7}}{4}$ = _____ = _____ = _____ = _____ = _____

5. $\dfrac{5\frac{3}{4}}{8}$ = _____ = _____ = _____

STEVE WISE SAYS:

1. Multiplication and division are inverse operations.

2. Multiplication can be thought of as a series of additions.

3. Division can be thought of as a series of subtractions.

4. In multiplication as the multiplier increases in size, so does the product.

5. In division as the divisor decreases in size, the quotient gets larger.

6. **(Rule #1)** To multiply fractions, multiply the numerators times numerators, and denominators times denominators.

7. To multiply a whole number by a fraction, express the whole number as a fraction, then follow rule #1.

8. To multiply a mixed number times a fraction, express the mixed number as a fraction, and follow rule #1.

9. To multiply mixed numbers, express both numbers as fractions, and follow rule #1.

10. The rule for division of fractions: Invert the divisor and multiply.

11. To change a mixed number to a fraction, multiply the denominator times the whole number and add the numerator.

CHAPTER SIX:

Make It Easy On Yourself

1 PREVIEW

In this program you'll see how many of the things that have already been discussed in the Adult Math Series fit together.

First, Martha and David have a session about cancellation. Martha learns that cancellation is a process of reducing the answer before you have one.

Later, Todd shares a discovery about cancellation that gets the students into a discussion that will become very important in later lessons. They talk about compound fractions, and how they fit into the scheme of things.

In the final scene, the students find out why the rule for division of fractions works.

Many of the ideas expressed in this program will have application in the lessons to come.

Important Vocabulary

Cancellation — In multiplication and division of fractions this is a process of simplifying a problem so it can be solved more easily.

Compound Fraction — This is a fraction within a fraction. It doesn't happen often in common fractions, but it is very common in decimals. The students in this program find out that fraction families are still important.

Intuition — This is a quality of the mind that allows you to know something without knowing why. It is very much like a "hunch."

Intuitive Thinking — Frank explains this process to the students to show them how to take advantage of their hunches.

Reciprocal — A reciprocal is a number that can be multiplied by another number so that the answer is 1. It is necessary to understand the reciprocal to explain the rule for division of fractions.

2 GOAL SETTING EXERCISE (Answers on page 226.)

1. Multiply these examples (reduce when possible).

A. $\dfrac{3}{4} \times \dfrac{1}{2} =$ **B.** $\dfrac{7}{8} \times \dfrac{1}{4} =$ **C.** $\dfrac{3}{8} \times \dfrac{2}{3} =$

D. $2 \times \dfrac{1}{3} =$

E. $5 \times \dfrac{3}{5} =$

F. $6\dfrac{1}{2} \times \dfrac{5}{6} =$

2. Divide these examples (reduce when possible).

A. $4 \div \dfrac{2}{3} =$

B. $6 \div \dfrac{3}{4} =$

C. $7 \div \dfrac{5}{8} =$

D. $\dfrac{3}{8} \div 4 =$

E. $4\dfrac{1}{4} \div \dfrac{4}{5} =$

F. $3\dfrac{1}{2} \div 2\dfrac{1}{3} =$

3. Solve these problems using cancellation. (You may still need to reduce some answers.)

A. $\dfrac{3}{4} \times \dfrac{8}{9} =$

B. $\dfrac{2}{3} \times \dfrac{1}{4} =$

C. $\dfrac{5}{8} \times \dfrac{2}{15} =$

D. $\dfrac{5}{8} \times \dfrac{4}{5} =$

E. $\dfrac{7}{9} \times \dfrac{3}{14} =$

F. $\dfrac{5}{6} \times \dfrac{4}{15} =$

4. Make fraction families for these compound fractions. Remember that the numerators increase by that number.

A. $\dfrac{2\frac{1}{2}}{\frac{1}{3}} =$ $=$ $=$ $=$

B. $\dfrac{\frac{5}{8}}{\frac{2}{3}} =$ $=$ $=$ $=$

C. $\dfrac{7\frac{1}{2}}{100} =$

5. Half of what number can be divided by $2\frac{1}{3}$ to get 3?

6. Martha broke a string of pearls. When she had found 16 of them, she knew that was only $\frac{2}{3}$ of the entire string. How many pearls were on the original string?

7. Bill was playing a video game. He found out he needed 3 quarters for $\frac{1}{3}$ of an hour. At that rate, how many quarters would he need for an hour?

GOAL PROFILE

Put a check mark in the box that fits your situation.

When You Watch the Program

☐ A. If you got them all right, you're some kind of math whiz.

Be sure you understand why it isn't necessary to cut up the sheep to divide them as Frank suggests.

☐ B. If you missed any part of number 1, then . . . .

Review Chapter Five page 61. Watch Martha carefully in the first scene.

☐ C. If you missed any part of number 2, then . . . .

Review Chapter Five page 62. Look at the rule for the division of fractions again. Bill has some help for you in scene three of the program.

☐ D. If you missed any part of number 3, then . . . .

Check your work to see if your errors are in reducing. If so, cancellation may be for you. Pay very close attention to the first scene.

☐ E.   If you missed any part of
        number 4, then . . . .

Be alert during scene two. Then before you work the Cumulative Quiz in this chapter, look at Chapter 5 page 66.

☐ F.   If you missed number 5,
        then . . . .

This is an inverse operation problem. Review Chapter Five. Frank talks about inverse operations in scene two of this program.

☐ G.   If you missed number 6,
        then . . . .

Study the rule for division of fractions before you view the program.

☐ H.   If you missed number 7,
        then . . . .

Study the problem again. In scene two Frank talks about compound fractions. As you listen, think about a fraction that says $\dfrac{\frac{3}{4}}{\frac{1}{3}}$.

3 NOW YOU ARE READY TO WATCH THE PROGRAM, "MAKE IT EASY ON YOURSELF."

4 REACT, PRACTICE, AND EXTEND. (Answers on page 226.)

Tips and Short Cuts

In this chapter we've broken up the practice to handle the three distinct scenes.

Scene One: Cancellation

Study this plan for cancellation. In cancellation you divide **both** a numerator and a denominator by the same number.

Ordinary way: **Cancellation:**

A. $\frac{3}{4} \times \frac{1}{6} = \textcircled{3} \quad \frac{3}{24} = \frac{1}{8}$

$$\frac{\overset{1}{\cancel{3}}}{4} \times \frac{1}{\underset{2}{\cancel{6}}} = \frac{1}{8}$$

B. $\frac{9}{10} \times \frac{4}{27} = \textcircled{9} \quad \frac{36}{270} = \textcircled{2} \quad \frac{4}{30} = \frac{2}{15}$

$$\frac{\overset{1}{\cancel{9}}}{\underset{5}{\cancel{10}}} \times \frac{\overset{2}{\cancel{4}}}{\underset{3}{\cancel{27}}} = \frac{2}{15}$$

As you can see, especially in the second example, cancellation keeps the numbers small and more manageable. It is much easier to find a common factor for small numbers than it is for large ones.

Practice: Now try to solve these by the cancellation method.

1. **A.** $\frac{7}{8} \times \frac{2}{7} =$ **B.** $\frac{2}{3} \times \frac{6}{7} =$ **C.** $\frac{5}{9} \times \frac{3}{10} =$

   D. $\frac{3}{5} \times \frac{5}{8} =$ **E.** $\frac{3}{8} \times \frac{4}{15} =$ **F.** $\frac{1}{4} \times \frac{2}{5} =$

Mixed numbers work the same way. First make improper fractions of the mixed numbers.

2. **A.** $2\frac{2}{3} \times 4\frac{1}{2} =$ **B.** $1\frac{3}{4} \times 1\frac{1}{7} =$

   C. $3\frac{3}{5} \times 1\frac{1}{9} =$ **D.** $4\frac{3}{8} \times 2\frac{2}{7} =$

E. $5\frac{5}{6} \times 2\frac{2}{5} =$

F. $1\frac{3}{5} \times \frac{5}{8} =$

Todd discovered that in a fraction problem that will cancel, the numerators can be traded, and the fractions simplified by reducing them. The effect is the same, but on some problems it might be easier, or this system could be used to check results.

Ordinary way: **Cancellation:**

$$\frac{5}{9} \times \frac{3}{5} = ③ \ \frac{15}{45} = ⑤ \ \frac{5}{15} = \frac{1}{3}$$

$$\overset{1}{\underset{3}{\cancel{5}}} \times \overset{1}{\underset{1}{\cancel{3}}} = \frac{1}{3}$$

Numerator trading:

$$\frac{5}{9} \times \frac{3}{5} = \frac{\overset{1}{\cancel{3}} \times \cancel{5}}{\underset{3}{\cancel{9}} \times \cancel{5}}$$

Remember: Both of these shortcuts work because of the multiplication principle which says sequence makes no difference ($4 \times 3 = 3 \times 4$). Also, in a problem that has both multiplication and division, it doesn't make any difference which operation comes first.

Solve these examples by using the system of trading numerators.

3. A. $\frac{2}{3} \times \frac{3}{4} =$ **B.** $\frac{5}{8} \times \frac{2}{5} =$ **C.** $\frac{3}{4} \times \frac{4}{5} =$

D. $\frac{7}{9} \times \frac{5}{7} =$ **E.** $\frac{11}{14} \times \frac{7}{11} =$ **F.** $\frac{6}{15} \times \frac{5}{6} =$

The important idea in the third scene has to do with two ways of looking at the division of fractions.

This problem answers more than one question.

$$12 \div \frac{1}{2} = 24$$

It can ask, "How many $\frac{1}{2}$'s are there in 12?" or it can ask, "How many half dollars are there in $12?"

The second question is harder to understand because it compares the fractional "pile" to a **whole**. Another way to ask the question is, "If 12 is $\frac{1}{2}$, what is 1?" or "If I had $12 and that was half enough to buy what I want, what is the cost?"

In order to do this mathematically, we use the reciprocal of the divisor. Here is Bill's explanation of the problem: $12 \div \frac{2}{3}$

First, he made a compound fraction out of it.

$\dfrac{\frac{12}{1}}{\frac{2}{3}}$ Instead of dividing 12 by $\frac{2}{3}$, he divided it by 1 by multiplying the $\frac{2}{3}$ by its reciprocal.

$\dfrac{\frac{12}{1}}{\frac{2}{3} \times \frac{3}{2}}$ **But** realizing that fractions are jealous, he did the same thing to the numerator.

$\dfrac{\frac{12}{1} \times \frac{3}{2}}{\frac{2}{3} \times \frac{3}{2}}$ This is the same as dividing by 1, which doesn't do anything except compare the problem to 1.

$\dfrac{\frac{12}{1} \times \frac{3}{2}}{1}$ All that is left is the same thing you would have if you inverted the divisor and multiplied.

A more mathematical way of stating the rule for the division of fractions is, "To divide by a fraction, multiply the divisor and the dividend by the reciprocal of the divisor."

In the examples below, write the reciprocals for the numbers listed.

4.   **A.** 2   **B.** $\frac{1}{2}$ **C.** $\frac{3}{4}$ **D.** $5\frac{1}{3}$ **E.** $\frac{1}{8}$

F. $\frac{9}{1}$ **G.** $\frac{3}{2}$ **H.** 6   **I.** $2\frac{1}{15}$ **J.** $\frac{1}{67}$

VOCABULARY MATCHING (Answers on page 227.)

Match the numbered words with the definitions.

1. Product   _____

2. Reciprocal   _____

3. Dividend   _____

4. Diameter   _____

5. Numeral   _____

6. Compound fraction   _____

7. Multiplier   _____

8. Cancellation   _____

A. A number that when multiplied by another gives the answer of 1.

B. In multiplication the number multiplied by.

C. The answer of a multiplication problem.

D. A fraction within a fraction.

E. Distance across a circle measured through the center.

F. The number to be divided.

G. A process of reducing fractions in multiplication and division **before** you multiply.

H. A way of expressing the idea of number.

CUMULATIVE QUIZ (Answers on page 227.)

1. Add these fractions and mixed numbers.

A. $\frac{1}{2} + \frac{2}{1} =$

B. $4\frac{1}{3} + \frac{3}{8} =$

C. $2\frac{1}{2} + 3\frac{1}{3} + 1\frac{1}{4} =$

D. $4\frac{7}{8} + 5\frac{2}{3} =$

E. $6\frac{1}{8} + \frac{1}{5} =$

F. $7\frac{1}{4} + 3\frac{4}{5} =$

2. Subtract these fractions and mixed numbers.

A. $\frac{7}{8} - \frac{1}{3} =$

B. $\frac{5}{9} - \frac{1}{3} =$

C. $\dfrac{3}{7} - \dfrac{1}{3} =$

D. $3\dfrac{1}{3} - \dfrac{7}{8} =$

E. $2\dfrac{1}{4} - 1\dfrac{15}{16} =$

F. $4\dfrac{1}{8} - 4\dfrac{1}{16} =$

3. Multiply or divide these fractions and mixed numbers according to the signs. (Cancel when you can, reduce when needed.)

A. $2\dfrac{1}{2} \times 3\dfrac{1}{3} =$

B. $6\dfrac{1}{2} \times \dfrac{5}{8} =$

C. $2\dfrac{1}{3} \div \dfrac{3}{4} =$

D. $4\dfrac{1}{3} \div 2\dfrac{1}{2} =$

E. $3\dfrac{1}{5} \times 6 =$

F. $6 \div 3\dfrac{1}{5} =$

G. $4 \times \dfrac{1}{15} =$

H. $2\dfrac{1}{3} \times 4 =$

4. A. $\dfrac{1}{3} \times \boxed{} = 12$ **B.** $7 \div \boxed{} = 21$ **C.** $4\dfrac{1}{2} \times \boxed{} = \dfrac{3}{8}$

5. $\dfrac{1}{3}$ of what number is 2 more than $\dfrac{1}{2}$ of 8?

6. Frank works $4\dfrac{1}{2}$ hours per day, 6 days a week, at the Adult School. How many hours does he work in a week's time?

7. David's son, Jimmy, is $\dfrac{1}{6}$ of David's age. Jimmy is 5 years old. How old is David? How old will both of them be when Jimmy is $\dfrac{1}{2}$ of David's age?

8. Bill bought a granola bar that weighed $\frac{3}{4}$ of a pound. It was divided into small sections that weighed $\frac{1}{32}$ of a pound each. How many sections were in the bar?

9. On a test Martha was able to answer $\frac{7}{8}$ of the questions correctly. If she got 56 of the questions right, how many questions were on the test?

10. It was announced that the United Way drive was $\frac{3}{4}$ of the way to reaching its goal of $1\frac{1}{2}$ million dollars. How much had been collected at that point?

My score on the Cumulative Quiz _____ (number right)

EXTENDING YOUR UNDERSTANDING (Answers on page 228.)

In fraction families we have left some of the numbers out. It might be interesting to include more of them in the family.

Here is a family for $\frac{1}{2}$ including some members that we don't usually see. Study this family and then complete the others listed.

$$\frac{1}{2} = \frac{1\frac{1}{2}}{3} = \frac{2}{4} = \frac{2\frac{1}{2}}{5} = \frac{3}{6} = \frac{3\frac{1}{2}}{7} = \frac{4}{8} = \frac{4\frac{1}{2}}{9} = \frac{5}{10}$$

1. $\frac{3}{4} = \frac{}{5} = \frac{}{6} = \frac{}{7} = \frac{}{8} = \frac{}{9} = \frac{}{10} = \frac{}{11} = \frac{}{12}$

2. $\frac{5}{6} = \frac{}{7} = \frac{}{8} = \frac{}{9} = \frac{}{10} = \frac{}{11} = \frac{}{12}$

3. $\frac{2}{3} = \frac{}{4} = \frac{}{5} = \frac{}{6} = \frac{}{7} = \frac{}{8} = \frac{}{9} = \frac{}{10}$

STEVE WISE SAYS:

1. Cancellation is used in multiplication and division of fractions to simplify the calculation. It is like reducing your answer before you have one.

2. Cancellation works because in a problem involving only multiplication and division, the sequence in which you do these operations doesn't matter.

3. Here are three ways to solve a multiplication of fractions problem:

   A. Multiply straight across and reduce the answer.

   $$\frac{3}{4} \times \frac{2}{3} = \frac{6}{12} = \frac{1}{2}$$

   B. Cancel or reduce before multiplying.

   $$\frac{\overset{1}{\cancel{3}}}{\underset{2}{\cancel{4}}} \times \frac{\overset{1}{\cancel{2}}}{\underset{1}{\cancel{3}}} = \frac{1}{2}$$

   C. Trade numerators and simplify the expression.

   $$\frac{3}{4} \times \frac{2}{3} = \frac{2}{4} \times \frac{\overset{1}{\cancel{3}}}{\underset{1}{\cancel{3}}} = \frac{2}{4} = \frac{1}{2}$$

4. Division of fractions can ask more than one question.

   $\frac{12}{1} \div \frac{1}{2}$ can ask, "How many $\frac{1}{2}$'s are there in twelve?"

5. Or it can ask, "What would this relationship of numbers be if I were dividing by 1?"

6. The rule for division of fractions, invert the divisor and multiply, is a short cut. What you are actually doing is multiplying the dividend and the divisor by the reciprocal of the divisor.

CHAPTER SEVEN:
The Point of Decimals

1 PREVIEW

This is a very fast moving program that will challenge your newly acquired detective skills. Be on the lookout for clues in everything you see and hear.

An important first "clue" has to do with the "ten-ness" of our number system. The very word *decimal* means ten. Decimal fractions, as our friends discover, are just an extension of the whole number system. They are fractions whose denominators are tens or multiples of ten.

The beauty of this arrangement can be seen in the ease of computing with decimal fractions. It is far more natural than working with common fractions.

The third scene deals with graphs, which are pictures of the decimal system.

Important Vocabulary

Abstract — Frank uses this word in explaining the number line. It is an idea, imaginary, it doesn't really exist except in our minds.

Annexing Zeroes — In this program this term is used to mean putting additional zeroes in a decimal where they are needed to allow the decimal point to be where it belongs.

Axis — In some graphs a line is drawn as a starting point. This line is called an axis.

Concrete — This is the opposite of abstract. It means something real, something you can touch.

Decimal Fractions — A fraction that has as its denominator ten or a multiple of ten. Decimal fractions are usually written in this form: .4, which is the same as $\frac{4}{10}$.

Decimal Understood — As the term is used in this program, it means that at the end of every whole number there is a decimal point even if it isn't written. The number 25 can be thought of as 0025.000. The decimal point is like a stop sign that says, "This is the end of the whole number. Anything from here on is a fraction."

Graph — A graph is a picture of numerical information. It is an easy way to show several related ideas at the same time.

Horizontal or Vertical Axis — In many line and bar graphs two lines are drawn so that several bits of information can be examined together. The one that is drawn up and down is the vertical axis. The one that is parallel to the ground is the horizontal axis.

Increment — In this program the word increment refers to a division on a graph. It can be thought of as a section of a line or a measurement.

Percent — Percent is a specialized decimal meaning "out of 100." 45% is another way of expressing .45.

Place Value — In our number system each place or column is given a value which is 10 times or $\frac{1}{10}$ the column on either side. Going left, each column is 10 times the previous. Going right, the columns are $\frac{1}{10}$ the value of the previous one.

Power of Ten — Because our number system is built around tens, sometimes we want to talk about tens multiplied by tens. This is called powers of ten. Ten to the third power, written 10^3, is equal to 1,000.

Proportionately — By now you should be well equipped to deal with this concept. It is the relationship between two number ideas. Fraction families are set up to be proportionate.

Reference Point — Again, in graphs, this is any point that can be identified numerically. In this program Frank talks about estimating "between the reference points."

2 GOAL SETTING EXERCISE (Answers on page 229.)

1. Change these fractions to decimals.

    A. $\frac{1}{4} = $.____   **B.** $\frac{3}{4} = $.____   **C.** $\frac{4}{5} = $.____

    D. $\frac{2}{3} = $.____   **E.** $\frac{7}{8} = $.____   **F.** $\frac{5}{6} = $.____

2. Change these decimals to fractions.

    A. .4 = ____   **B.** .75 = ____   **C.** .14 = ____

    D. .375 = ____   **E.** .04 = ____   **F.** $.16\frac{2}{3} = $ ____

3. Add these decimals. (Rewrite them on a scrap piece of paper.)

    A. 23.04 + 2.3 = ____   **B.** 7.5 + 14.006 = ____   **C.** 25 + 2.372 = ____

D. $17.6 + .004 =$ _____   **E.** $23.33\frac{1}{3} + 6.66\frac{2}{3} =$ _____   **F.** $2.46 + 21.50 =$ _____

4. Subtract these decimals.

   A. $26.21 - 12.04 =$ _____   **B.** $17.563 - 3.4 =$ _____   **C.** $22.003 - 1.25 =$ _____

   D. $14 - 6.936 =$ _____   **E.** $24.03 - 14.406 =$ _____   **F.** $5.04 - 5.004 =$ _____

5. Multiply these decimals.

   A. $22.6 \times 2.06 =$ _____   **B.** $12.4 \times .003 =$ _____   **C.** $26.1 \times 2.4 =$ _____

   D. $14.36 \times 1.4 =$ _____   **E.** $2.48 \times 2.48 =$ _____   **F.** $17 \times 2.5 =$ _____

6. Divide these decimals.

   A. $.24 \div .04 =$ _____   **B.** $38 \div 2.5 =$ _____   **C.** $44 \div .33 =$ _____

   D. $.28 \div 14 =$ _____   **E.** $2.6 \div 1.3 =$ _____   **F.** $.66 \div 2.2 =$ _____

7. What decimal fraction plus .50 is the decimal equivalent to $\frac{3}{4}$?

8. Todd read the odometer on his car before and after a trip. Here are the readings. How long was the trip?
   Before: 082460.7
   After: 083772.4

9. Sue spent 35% of her pay one week to get her car repaired. If her paycheck was $200.00, how much did it cost for the repairs?

10. This is a graph that tells how a club spent its money for the year. If the club had a budget of $1,000.00, how much money was spent for each item?

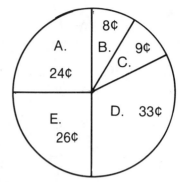

A. Decorations   _____

B. Utilities   _____

C. Janitor   _____

D. Food   _____

E. Entertainment   _____

GOAL PROFILE

Put a check mark in the box that fits your situation.

When You Watch the Program

☐ A. If you got them all right, Marvelous!

Enjoy the program. There are some concepts in it that will help move you on to bigger and better things.

☐ B. If you missed any part of number 1, then . . . .

Remember that the line between the terms of a fraction means "divided by."

☐ C. If you missed any part of number 2, then . . . .

Think about fraction families as you watch the program.

☐ D. If you missed any part of number 3, then . . . .

Listen carefully to Todd's explanation of the procedures for adding decimals.

☐ E. If you missed any part of number 4, then . . . .

Listen to Sue as she points out the pitfalls of subtracting decimal fractions.

☐ F. If you missed any part of number 5, then . . . .

Listen to Bill and Steve Wise. Did you put the decimal point in the wrong place in the answer?

☐ G. If you missed any part of
        number 6, then . . . .   Martha shows us how to divide. Watch
                                                        her carefully. Review Chapter Six where
                                                        it talks about making fractions behave
                                                        like whole numbers.

☐ H. If you missed number 7,
        then . . . .   Be certain you understand how to
                                                        change common fractions to decimals.
                                                        There is a brief discussion of inverse
                                                        operations in this program also.

☐ I. If you missed number 8,
        then . . . .   Study Sue's approach to subtraction.

☐ J. If you missed number 9,
        then . . . .   Chapter Six said the word "of" means to
                                                        multiply. The same is true for percent.
                                                        50% of something means .50 times that
                                                        number. Study Bill's plan for
                                                        multiplying.

☐ K. If you missed any part of
        number 10, then . . . .   Be alert to the scene that talks about
                                                        graphs.

3 NOW YOU ARE READY TO WATCH THE PROGRAM, "THE POINT OF DECIMALS."

4 REACT, PRACTICE, AND EXTEND. (Answers on page 230.)

Tips and Short Cuts

Before you work the practice section, look at the math procedures that were talked about in this program.

Reading a decimal fraction

The numeral takes its name and value from the column it is in.

In the example above the 1 means 1×10.

the 2 means 2×1.

the 3 means $3 \times \dfrac{1}{10}$ or $\dfrac{3}{10}$

the 4 means $4 \times \dfrac{1}{100}$ or $\dfrac{4}{100}$

the 5 means $5 \times \dfrac{1}{1000}$ or $\dfrac{5}{1000}$

This number is read twelve AND three hundred forty-five thousandths.

Changing a common fraction to a decimal fraction

You have many tools now to change a common fraction to a decimal fraction. It can be done by using:

Fraction family	Factoring	Division
$\dfrac{2}{5} = \dfrac{4}{10} = .4$	$\overset{25}{\bigcirc}\ \dfrac{3}{4} = \dfrac{75}{100} = .75$	$\dfrac{4}{5} = 5\overline{)4.0}^{\,.8}$

Changing a decimal fraction to a common fraction

Reduction method

$$.4 = \enspace ② \enspace \frac{4}{10} = \frac{2}{5}$$

Cancellation

$$.25 = \frac{\overset{1}{\cancel{25}}}{\underset{4}{\cancel{100}}} = \frac{1}{4}$$

Adding and subtracting decimal fractions

This is a very natural process. Be certain, however, that the decimal points are lined up before starting to solve the problem.

```
   24.06              13.600
 +  2.7             –  2.443
 ───────            ────────
   26.76              11.157
     ↑                   ↑
(points even)       (points even)
```

Sue says to annex zeros here to make it even. Not necessary, just neat.

When the decimal points are lined up in this manner, you automatically add or subtract the same kind of numbers from each other. (Ones and ones, tens and tens, tenths and tenths, etc.)

Multiplication of decimals

Once again, the manner in which the problem is set up is important. With multiplication the right column should be even. The reason is the same as for addition. The partial products must line up so that you are adding like quantities. (Ones to ones, tens to tens, tenths to tenths, and so on.)

Placing the decimal point in the product is the next thing to be careful about. Count the number of places to the right of the decimal in both the multiplicand and the multiplier, and count off that many places from the right in the product.

```
      4 . 3 2 6
  ×       6 . 7  ← 4 places
  ─────────────
      3 0 2 8 2   partial products
    2 5 9 5 6
  ─────────────
    2 8.9 8 4 2
        ↑
    4 places (right to left)
```

```
      1 . 2
  × . 0 0 3  ← 4 places
  ──────────
  . 0 0 3 6
      ↗
```
Annex enough zeroes to place point in the right position.

Estimation helps you to know if the point is in the right place.

The problem on the left is going to be more than 4 × 6, but less than 5 × 6. You should know from this that the answer isn't 2.89842, nor is it 289.842.

Division of decimal fractions

There should be no mystery now as to why we move the decimal point when dividing decimal fractions. It is the same reason we invert the divisor when dividing common fractions. It is so we can deal with whole numbers.

In this problem,

$$.25 \overline{)\ 75}$$

.25 has the *same numerical relationship* to 75 as 25 does to 7,500. Both numbers are one hundred times bigger so they can be divided as whole numbers.

$$.25 \overline{)\ 75.00.}$$

Seen as a common fraction this problem would look like this:

$$\frac{75}{1} \div \frac{25}{100} = \frac{75}{1} \times \frac{100}{25} = \frac{7500}{25}$$

This step is what happens in decimals and does the same thing as moving the decimal in both the divisor and the dividend. It says, "75 × 100 ÷ 25."

So does this, $.25 \overline{)\ 75.00.}$

For more understanding, look at it this way. If you were to put the decimal points in the partial products, the decimal points line up just as if it were a simple addition of decimals problem.

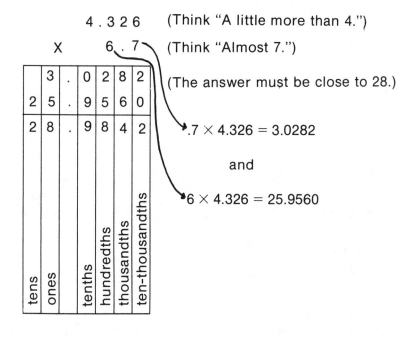

4 . 3 2 6 (Think "A little more than 4.")

X 6 . 7 (Think "Almost 7.")

(The answer must be close to 28.)

.7 × 4.326 = 3.0282

and

6 × 4.326 = 25.9560

Here are the steps in dividing a decimal fraction:

Step One: Move the decimal point in the divisor making it a whole number.

$$.435\overline{)\,68}\qquad\text{(Actually multiplying by 1000 in this case.)}$$

Step Two: Move the decimal point the same number of places in the dividend, using more zeroes if necessary. Place the decimal point in the quotient right above the new decimal placement in the dividend.

$$.435\overline{)\,68.000}\qquad\text{(Actually multiplying by 1000 in this case.)}$$

Step Three: Divide as if they are whole numbers.

```
         156.321
435) 68000.000
     435
     2450
     2175
      2750
      2610
       1400
       1305
        950
        870
         800
         435
         365
```

One more thing. Decimals often contain common fractions. For instance, $.37\frac{1}{2}$ or $7.5\frac{1}{3}$. This is a form of compound fractions.

Practice: (Answers on page 230.)

1. Change these fractions to decimals (some may be decimals and common fractions).

   A. $\dfrac{1}{3} =$ _____   **B.** $\dfrac{7}{9} =$ _____   **C.** $\dfrac{10}{11} =$ _____   **D.** $\dfrac{11}{14} =$ _____   **E.** $\dfrac{7}{8} =$ _____

2. Add these decimal fractions.

    A. $1.3 + 2.04 = $ _____   **B.** $3.68 + 2.004 = $ _____   **C.** $13.17 + 16.83 = $ _____

    D. $45.06 + 23.64 = $ _____   **E.** $77.7 + 22.3 = $ _____   **F.** $36.5 + 4.05 = $ _____

3. Subtract these decimals.

    A. $6.03 - 2.4 = $ _____   **B.** $9.004 - 6.9 = $ _____   **C.** $3.21 - 1.48 = $ _____

    D. $266.4 - .003 = $ _____   **E.** $15.6 - 12.9 = $ _____   **F.** $66.6 - 51.9 = $ _____

4. Multiply these examples.

    A. $2.3 \times .04 = $ _____   **B.** $17.1 \times 2.6 = $ _____   **C.** $.382 \times .24 = $ _____

    D. $6.3 \times .024 = $ _____   **E.** $31 \times .06 = $ _____   **F.** $.21 \times .02 = $ _____

5. Divide these problems.

    A. $.23 \div 1.3 = $ _____   **B.** $17 \div .25 = $ _____   **C.** $6 \div .38 = $ _____

    D. $45 \div .15 = $ _____   **E.** $24 \div .235 = $ _____   **F.** $.26 \div .13 = $ _____

6. Percentages are a specialized form of decimal fractions. Percents are always expressed as hundredths.

    $.35 = 35\%$ $68\% = .68$

To change a decimal to percent, move the decimal point two places to the right and use the percent sign.

    $.52 = 52\%$ $.375 = 37.5\%$ $.075 = 7.5\%$

Practice changing these decimals to percents.

A. .35 = _____   **B.** 7.8 = _____   **C.** .06 = _____

D. 1.23 = _____   **E.** .035 = _____   **F.** .25 = _____

7. Practice changing these percents to decimals. (Be certain that you **trade** the % for the decimal point — 62% = .62.)

A. 43% = _____   **B.** 57.6% = _____   **C.** $87\frac{1}{2}$% = _____   **D.** 4.4% = _____

E. 5% = _____   **F.** 163% = _____   **G.** .03% = _____   **H.** 50% = _____

Note: In multiplying decimals we often say, "Round off to the nearest .... " In division we say, "Carry to three places beyond the decimal point."

Example: 24.2337 rounded off to the nearest $\frac{1}{1000}$ is 24.234. Since the "7" is 5 or more, you increase the next column to the left by 1, and drop the "7."

8. 72.86 rounded to nearest tenth _____

9. 32.09 rounded to nearest tenth _____

10. 66.249 rounded to nearest hundredth _____

11. .23278 rounded to nearest ten-thousandth _____

In division this problem could be carried on forever and never come out even. It doesn't make any sense to carry it beyond a few decimals. Make the remainder a fraction.

$$
\begin{array}{r}
58.111\overset{1}{9} \\
.36\overline{)21.00\,0000} \\
18\,0 \\
\hline
3\,00 \\
2\,96 \\
\hline
40 \\
36 \\
\hline
40 \\
36 \\
\hline
4
\end{array}
\qquad \frac{4}{36} = \frac{1}{9}
$$

CUMULATIVE QUIZ (Answers on page 231.)

1. Solve these problems (watch the signs).

A. $\dfrac{1}{4} \times \dfrac{3}{8} = $ _____

B. $\dfrac{2}{3} + \dfrac{1}{2} = $ _____

C. $\dfrac{3}{4} \div \dfrac{1}{2} = $ _____

D. $1\dfrac{7}{8} + 2\dfrac{1}{2} = $ _____

E. $2\dfrac{1}{3} - 1\dfrac{7}{8} = $ _____

F. $6 - 2\dfrac{3}{5} = $ _____

2. Addition of decimals.

A. $3.68 + 4.2 = $ _____   **B.** $6.24 + 3.06 = $ _____   **C.** $7.02 + 3.98 = $ _____

D. $4.006 + 3.4 = $ _____   **E.** $4.25 + 3.6 = $ _____   **F.** $6.3 + 3.7 = $ _____

3. Subtraction of decimals.

A. $2.5 - 1.03 = $ _____   **B.** $22.45 - 6.84 = $ _____   **C.** $4.06 - 2.96 = $ _____

D. $6.7 - 4.02 = $ _____   **E.** $2.2 - 1.9 = $ _____   **F.** $.044 - .036 = $ _____

4. Multiplication of decimals.

    A. $28.3 \times .36 =$ _____   **B.** $.23 \times .18 =$ _____   **C.** $3.1416 \times 7 =$ _____

5. Work these percent problems.

    A. 20% of 55 = _____   **B.** 33% of 2.6 = _____   **C.** 28% of .246 = _____

6. 20% of what number is 1.6 more than 2.4?

7. Bill was measuring some steel rods. One rod was 1.038 inches in diameter. Another was 1.275 inches in diameter. What was the difference in diameters?

8. Our money system is based on decimals. What is the common fraction equivalent of the coins we use? (Compared to a dollar)

    A. 1¢ = _____   **B.** 5¢ = _____   **C.** 10¢ = _____   **D.** 25¢ = _____   **E.** 50¢ = _____

9. 55% of the people in our country are female. If our population is 220 million, how many women are in our country?

10. A large newspaper had this graph made. Study it, and then answer the questions.

Circulation (in 10 thousands)

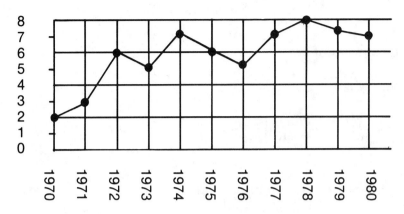

A. What was the circulation in 1970?

B. What was the circulation in 1974?

C. What is the difference between 1970 and 1974?

D. Express this difference as a common fraction.

E. What is the decimal fraction that expresses this difference?

F. How much difference is there between 1970 and 1976?

STEVE WISE SAYS:

1. Decimal fractions are an extension of the whole number system.

2. Decimal fractions have denominators that are always ten or powers of ten.

3. Say "and" only where the decimal point is.

4. To add or subtract a decimal fraction, be certain that all the decimal points are lined up under one another.

5. To multiply by a decimal fraction, set up the problem so that the right side is lined up.

6. To place the decimal point in the right place in the product, count the number to the right of the decimal point in the multiplicand and the multiplier, and count off the same number from the right in the product.

7. A graph is a pictorial way of showing quantities or numerical information.

8. Graphs give a quick idea of a situation.

9. Graphs enable you to make comparisons that would otherwise be very difficult to express.

10. When reading graphs, always look for the key to see how much the various increments are really talking about.

CHAPTER EIGHT:
Keeping Things In Proportion

1 PREVIEW

Martha is excited! She was actually able to help her neighbor's daughter with her math homework. You can imagine how fulfilling this was for Martha after all the trouble she's had with number ideas.

Ratio and proportion still bother her a little, though. She and David have a little session that clears up a few things for her, but leaves her with a perplexing question that is answered later.

In the last scene, the students, left alone in Frank's absence, find that if they pool their knowledge they can figure out some pretty difficult number relationships and solve problems that none of them thought they could.

Important Vocabulary

Balance — In this program the word is used to talk about equality. Both sides of an equal sign must always be equal even if you do "something" with the numbers there.

Colon — This punctuation mark (:) is used in ratio problems instead of the line used in a fraction. $\frac{4}{5}$ as a common fraction can be expressed as the ratio 4 : 5. It is read, "Four to five."

Percent — Decimal fractions with denominators of 100 are often written as percent. It is a way of looking at a number as a part of 100.

Proportion — This math idea is a way of thinking about two ratios. It answers a question like, "Two is to three as what is to nine?" ($\frac{2}{3} = \frac{N}{9}$)

Ratio — This is a way of comparing numbers by the process of division. Common fractions are a type of ratio. What we have been calling fraction or rational families are actually series of ratios.

Simplify — As it is used in this chapter it means about the same thing as reducing fractions to their lowest terms, except it refers to ratio and proportion.

2 GOAL SETTING EXERCISE (Answers on page 232.)

1. There are several ways to express fractions. Below are some common fractions. Express them first as decimal fractions and then as percent.

   Sample: $\frac{1}{2} = .5 = 50\%$

   A. $\frac{1}{3} =$ _____ = _____

   B. $\frac{2}{5} =$ _____ = _____

   C. $\frac{7}{8} =$ _____ = _____

   D. $\frac{5}{6} =$ _____ = _____

2. Simplify these ratio problems.

   Sample: $\frac{3}{9} = 1 : 3$

   A. $\frac{4}{16} =$ _____

   B. $\frac{20}{5} =$ _____

   C. $\frac{7}{56} =$ _____

   D. $\frac{14}{2} =$ _____

   E. $\frac{68}{17} =$ _____

   F. $\frac{35}{14} =$ _____

   G. $\frac{6}{19.8} =$ _____

3. Find the missing numbers.

   A. $.35 \times 8 =$ _____

   B. $.14 \times .6 =$ _____

   C. _____ $\times .35 = 9.45$

   D. $1.5 \times$ _____ $= 3.6$

4. Fill out this bar graph with the information given.

    At the shop where he works, Bill spent the week packing small parts. On Monday he packaged 200 parts, Tuesday 250, Wednesday 325, Thursday 375, and Friday 310. (Shade in the bars to the proper height.)

IN HUNDREDS

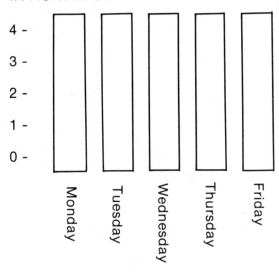

5. 25% of a number is 10 less than 50% of the same number. What is the number?

6. Todd was fooling around with some numbers, and found that multiplying by .25 was the same as dividing by 4 (40 × .25 = 10 & 40 ÷ 4 = 10). What whole number would you divide by to get the same answer as multiplying by these decimals?

    A. .20 − _____   **B.** $.33\frac{1}{3}$ − _____   **C.** $.16\frac{2}{3}$ − _____

    D. .50 − _____   **E.** $11\frac{1}{9}$ − _____

7. If Frank drove 385 miles in 7 hours, how many could he drive in 1 hour?

8. Sue said she read 75% of a book. She had read 300 pages. How many pages were in the book?

GOAL PROFILE

Put a check mark in the box that fits your situation.

When You Watch the Program

☐ A.   If you got them all right, then
. . . . . relax and enjoy the show.   You might wonder about David's statement about division being like ratio.

☐ B.   If you missed any part of number 1, then . . . .   Pay close attention as Martha helps Jenny.

☐ C.   If you missed any part of number 2, then . . . .   Martha and David will help you with this process.

☐ D.   If you missed any part of number 3, then . . . .   What did David mean when he asked Martha, "How did you get permission to divide?"

☐ E.   If you missed any part of number 4, then . . . .   Review Chapter Seven about graphs. Remember that the first problem the students solve in the third scene is a result of a graph problem.

☐ F.   If you missed any part of number 5, then . . . .   Draw a picture of how this must be, then pay very close attention to the program.

☐ G.   If you missed any part of number 6, then . . . .   Review page 86. Jenny and Martha hint at the solution. Bill does too in the third scene.

☐ H.   If you missed number 7, then . . . .   What **did** David mean when Martha asked if division was like ratio?

☐ I.   If you missed number 8, then . . . .   Review division of decimals in Chapter Seven. Study scene three.

3 NOW YOU ARE READY TO WATCH THE PROGRAM, "KEEPING THINGS IN PROPORTION."

4 REACT, PRACTICE, AND EXTEND. (Answers on page 233.)

Before you do the practice section, let's make sure you understand some of the important things that you just saw on the TV.

Steve Wise used this example to explain ratio. "There were 15 horses in a stable. Five of them were white. What is the ratio of **white** horses **to all** the horses?" He said it could be written as the fraction $\frac{5}{15}$, or as the ratio 5 : 15, or simplified to 1 : 3.

The order in which the terms are mentioned is important.

White to all

1 : 3

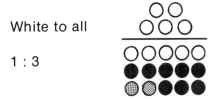

This means, as Steve Wise said, "One out of every three horses is white." If the question had been, "What is the ratio of **all** the horses to the **white**?" the answer would have been different.

All to white

3 : 1

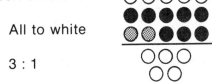

This means out of every 3 horses, 1 is white.

Answer these questions about the horses. (Answers on page 233.)

1. What is the ratio of white horses to all **other** colors? (Not the same as the total.)

2. Of the horses, 2 were pintos. What is the ratio of pintos to white?

3. What is the ratio of pintos to the total?

4. What is the ratio of pintos and whites together to all other colors?

There are two slightly different ideas expressed here.

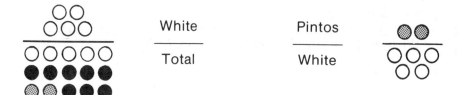

$$\frac{White}{Total}$$

$$\frac{Pintos}{White}$$

White horses to all

Pintos to white

The white ones are included in **both** numerator and denominator.

This is like David's illustration of books and people.

   CAUTION: When you write a ratio, the first number mentioned is the numerator of the fraction.
   RULE: To simplify a ratio, divide the numerator by the denominator.

$$\frac{3}{9} = 3 \div 9 = 1 : 3 \text{ ratio}$$

There can be fractional ratios too. The same rule applies:

$$\frac{\frac{2}{3}}{\frac{3}{4}} = \frac{2}{3} \div \frac{3}{4} = \frac{2}{3} \times \frac{4}{3} = \frac{8}{9} = 8 : 9$$

A fraction in its lowest terms is the same as the ratio $(\frac{1}{2} = 1{:}2 \text{ ratio}; \frac{3}{5} = 3{:}5 \text{ ratio})$.

PRACTICE: (Answers on page 233.)

1. Simplify these ratios.

A. $\frac{5}{10} =$ _____   B. $\frac{13}{52} =$ _____   C. $\frac{\frac{3}{4}}{\frac{7}{8}} =$ _____   D. $\frac{5}{9} =$ _____

PROPORTION

   Ratio, as you have seen, is thinking about a relationship of two numbers. Proportion is an extension of that idea.
   The illustration, David told Martha, had to do with a bicycle. It was a ratio of 2 : 3. Every time the pedals went around two times, the wheels went around three times. The question can be asked then, "At that rate (ratio) how many times would the wheels go around if I pedaled 16 times?" You can use a fraction family to find this out.

$$\frac{2}{3} = \frac{4}{6} = \frac{6}{9} = \frac{8}{12} = \frac{10}{15} = \frac{12}{18} = \frac{14}{21} = \frac{16}{24}$$

The proof of proportion can be shown by using two members of the same fraction family and cross multiplying.

$$\begin{matrix} & 12 \\ \frac{2}{3} & \diagdown \frac{4}{6} \\ & 12 \end{matrix} \quad \text{so} \quad \begin{matrix} & 12 \\ \frac{2}{3} & \diagdown \frac{N}{6} \\ & 12 \end{matrix} \quad \text{What number times } 3 = 12?$$

Proportions, however, don't always fall on the number line at exactly the spot of an even multiple. The illustration below demonstrates this.

$$\frac{3}{4} \diagdown \frac{N}{22} \qquad 3 \times 22 = 66$$

$$66 \qquad 4 \times \underline{\quad} = 66$$

$$\frac{3}{4} = \frac{14.5}{26} \quad \text{Read: 3 is to 4 as 14.5 is to 26.}$$

This model shows you how to solve proportion problems.

$$\frac{4}{9} = \frac{N}{14}$$

Step 1: $4 \times 14 = 56$

Step 2: $9 \times N = 9N$

Step 3: $9N = 56$

Step 4: $56 \div 9 = N$

$$N = 6\frac{2}{9}$$

2. Now solve these proportion problems.

A. $\dfrac{4}{7} = \dfrac{N}{2.3}$ 　　 B. $\dfrac{6.3}{2.5} = \dfrac{14}{N}$ 　　 C. $\dfrac{.35}{7} = \dfrac{N}{2.4}$ 　　 D. $\dfrac{\frac{2}{3}}{\frac{5}{8}} = \dfrac{\frac{3}{4}}{N}$

E. $\dfrac{2}{7.3} = \dfrac{N}{4}$ 　　 F. $\dfrac{6.3}{\frac{2}{3}} = \dfrac{N}{4}$

INVERSE OPERATIONS

In the final scene, one of the most helpful tools in the "thinking" of math is used.

3. Let's go over the examples like our friends used to discover how this technique works. We'll talk our way through the first one, then you can complete the examples yourself.

N + 4.5 = 7.25   If N + 4.25 = 7.25, then 7.25 − 4.5 = N.   N = 2.75
Notice that the "inverse" of the operation given (in this case addition) is used to find the solution.

A. N − 3.6 = 14.3

B. 4.6 × N = 10.58

C. N ÷ 4.3 = 5.7

D. N × 10.4 = 2.6

REMEMBERING THE THINGS TO REMEMBER

A ratio is a way of looking at two numbers by using division.
A proportion is comparing two ratios.
Unknowns in a problem can be found by using inverse operations.

VOCABULARY MATCHING (Answers on page 234.)

1. Identity element _____   **A.** $\frac{2}{3}$ as $\frac{10}{15}$
   (for multiplication)

2. Mixed number _____   **B.** $3\frac{1}{4} = 2\frac{5}{4}$

$-2\frac{3}{4} = 2\frac{3}{4}$

3. Rational family _____

$\frac{2}{4} = \frac{1}{2}$

4. Proportion _____

C. :

5. Re-grouping _____

6. Colon _____   **D.** 2   3   5

7. Common fraction _____
      E. .675

8. Decimal fraction _____
      F. $2\frac{3}{4}$

9. Divisor _____

10. Product _____   **G.** 16 $\overline{}$ 64

11. Number line _____   **H.** $\frac{2}{3}, \frac{4}{6}, \frac{6}{9}, \frac{8}{12}, \frac{10}{15}$

12. Inverse operation _____

I. $2 \times 8 = 16$

J. 0 —— $\frac{1}{4}$ —— $\frac{1}{2}$ —— $\frac{3}{4}$ —— 1

K. 1

L. $\frac{1}{3}$

CUMULATIVE QUIZ (Answers on page 234.)

1. Multiply these decimal fractions.

A. $.263 \times 1.43 =$ _____

B. $4.36 \times 2.3 =$ _____

C. $57.02 \times .35 =$ _____

D. $36.002 \times .006 =$ _____

E. $2.7 \times .04 =$ _____

F. $.16 \times .04 =$ _____

2. Divide these decimal fractions.

A. $24 \div .36 =$ _____

B. $3.7 \div 1.2 =$ _____

C. $2.08 \div .07 =$ _____

D. $.35 \div 12.6 =$ _____

E. $27 \div .004 =$ _____

F. $73 \div .14 =$ _____

3. Change these fractions to percentages (carry to two places beyond decimal point).

A. $\dfrac{12}{17} =$ _____

B. $\dfrac{17}{12} =$ _____

C. $\dfrac{1}{14} =$ _____

D. $\dfrac{5}{7} =$ _____

E. $\dfrac{3}{8} =$ _____

F. $\dfrac{5}{4} =$ _____

4. Simplify these ratio examples.

A. $\dfrac{\frac{2}{3}}{\frac{3}{4}}$

B. $\dfrac{\frac{5}{8}}{4}$

C. $\dfrac{5}{1\frac{1}{3}}$

5. Solve for the unknowns in these proportion examples.

   A. $\dfrac{3}{2.5} = \dfrac{N}{7}$ **B.** $\dfrac{1\frac{1}{8}}{4} = \dfrac{9}{N}$ **C.** $\dfrac{5}{2.3} = \dfrac{N}{7}$

6. Use the process of inverse operations to solve these problems.

   A. $4.5 \div N = .72$ **B.** $\dfrac{3}{8} \times N = .09$ **C.** $N \div 3 = 50$

7. Todd was getting an enlargement made of a photograph of his family. The picture measures 3 inches by 5 inches. When it is enlarged, the longer side will be 18 inches. Since enlargements are proportionate, how long will the shorter side be?

8. For years Sue has followed a unique savings plan. For every dollar she spends for gas, she puts a nickel in an antique bank her grandfather gave her. What is the ratio of gas purchased to savings? What is the percent of savings?

9. Baseball batting averages are figured on hits per times at bat. A player who gets three hits for ten times at bat is said to have a batting average of three hundred (.300). With any two of these numbers you can find the other one. Fill out the batting average chart below.

PLAYER	TIMES AT BAT	HITS	AVERAGE
A	50	_____	.140
B	84	_____	.286
C	_____	21	.244
D	92	27	_____
E	_____	16	.229

10. The formula for finding the area of a rectangle is length X width. Martha's kitchen is $12\frac{1}{2}$ feet long and $10\frac{1}{3}$ feet wide. How many square feet of floor covering will she need to cover it?

Cumulative Quiz score _____ (number right)

EXTENDING YOUR UNDERSTANDING (Answers on page 235.)

The worksheet Jenny was working on in Martha's kitchen had a drawing that looked like this:

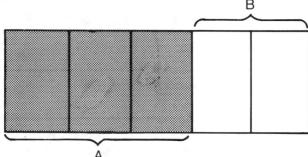

It is to show that in a whole divided into five pieces there are $\frac{5}{5}$. In the case above $\frac{3}{5}$ are shaded and $\frac{2}{5}$ are not. There is, however, another relationship. There is a ratio of 2 : 3 in this same picture.

Often in math these parts are seen as a whole.

Answer these questions:

1. What is $\frac{2}{3}$ of A?

2. What is A + $\frac{2}{3}$ of A?

3. If each section had a value of 10¢, what would be the value of A? B?

4. If you bought A for $.30 and sold it for $\frac{2}{3}$ more than you paid for it, how much would you have sold it for?

5. If you had $.75 and you were given $\frac{1}{3}$ of that amount, how much would you have?

6. If you had the total amount from number 5, what part of that could you give away and be back where you started?

There is another kind of proportion. It is called inverse proportion. See what you can do with this problem.

7. Two men can do a job in 6 hours. How long would it take 4 men to do the same job?

STEVE WISE SAYS:

1. Ratio is a way of looking at the relationship of two numbers. It compares them by division.

2. Proportion is a way of looking at two ratios that are equivalent. You are asked to find the missing element in the relationship.

3. Proportion problems are solved by a process called cross multiplication. This means to multiply the numerator of one fraction by the denominator of the other fraction.

4. Percents are fractions with denominators of one hundred.

5. To change a common fraction directly to a percent, use this system.

$$\frac{3}{4} \times \frac{100}{1} = \frac{300}{4} = 75\%$$

CHAPTER NINE:

Playing The Percentages

1 **PREVIEW**

All around us, everyone seems to be playing the percentages. Newspapers, magazines, TV, and conversation are filled with the word *percent*.

In this program our friends find out how to compute all the possible types of percentage problems.

In the first scene Frank and Todd develop all the formulas needed to solve percent problems. Later, when the rest of the class arrives, they practice all the cases.

As the class starts to leave, Bill makes a strange bet with Frank and Todd that will allow them to experience the percentage revolution in a unique way.

Important Vocabulary

Review the words in Chapter Eight. The only new words you'll come across are:

Equation — An equation is a statement of equality. $2 + 3 = 5$ is an equation. It means that the quantity on both sides of the equals sign is the same.

Formula — As it is used in this program, it means a plan for solving problems.

2 **GOAL SETTING EXERCISE** (Answers on page 236.)

1. Multiply these percent problems.

   A. 35% of 44   **B.** 26% of 88

   C. 98% of 245   **D.** 32% of 29

2. Divide these percent problems.

   A. 66 ÷ 14%   **B.** 28 ÷ 4%

   C. 124 ÷ 146%   **D.** .35 ÷ 15%

3. Divide these numbers. Change the answers to percent.

    A. $35 \div 14$ **B.** $26 \div 69$

    C. $14 \div 35$ **D.** $16 \div 246$

4. Solve these percent problems.

    A. $12 \div 24 =$ _____ %   **B.** $36 \times 20\% =$ _____

    C. $44 \div 18\% =$ _____

5. 20% of what number is 1 more than 10% of 100?

6. Sue's daughter graduated from high school last year. She said that 40% of her class went to college. If there were 260 students in her graduating class, how many went to college?

7. Bill took a math test that had 80 problems on it. He got 78 of them right. What percent is that?

8. Todd moved 40% of the stock in one storeroom to another. If he moved 160 gallons of paint, how many were in the storeroom to begin with?

GOAL PROFILE

Put a check mark in the box that fits your situation.

When You Watch the Program

☐ A. If you got them all right, then
   . . . you're a whiz at percentage.   See if Todd's one formula is enough for you.

☐ B. If you missed any part of
   number 1, then . . . .   Review Chapter Seven. Be sure you know how to multiply decimals before you watch the program.

☐ C. If you missed any part of
number 2 then ....

Review Chapter Seven. Remember that dividing by a percent is like dividing by a decimal.

☐ D. If you missed any part of
number 3, then ....

Did you make the problem into a fraction first? If you did, Jenny's system for getting a percent in Chapter Eight might help.

☐ E. If you missed any part of
number 4, then ....

Be sure to watch carefully as Frank explains each type of percentage problem.

☐ F. If you missed number 5,
then ....

Review inverse operations in Chapter Five. Follow Todd's thought process as he talks about the house he and his wife want to buy.

☐ G. If you missed number 6,
then ....

Pay particular attention to type two percentage problems. (Percent times the whole equals part.)

☐ H. If you missed number 7,
then ....

This is a type one percentage problem. You have the whole and the part given. You are asked to find the percent. Todd explains this problem in the TV program.

☐ I. If you missed number 8,
then ....

This is a division problem (type 3). You are given the part and the percent, and asked to find the whole. Sue has a good way to remember when to do this operation.

3 NOW YOU ARE READY TO WATCH THE PROGRAM, "PLAYING THE PERCENTAGES."

4 REACT, PRACTICE AND EXTEND. (Answers on page 236.)

Tips And Short Cuts

Here, once again, is the general case formula for percentage.

$$\frac{Part}{Whole} = Percent$$

This general formula can be broken down into three separate plans depending on which element is missing. Here are the three cases and a few practice examples for each one.

Type 1:

$$\frac{Part}{Whole} = \underline{\hspace{2cm}}$$

In this one you are trying to find the percent (fraction or decimal).

Martha is sending invitations to her friends. She needs to send 64 of them, and she has completed 48 of them. What percentage has she completed?

$$\frac{48}{64} = 64\overline{)48.00} \quad .75 = 75\%$$

```
            .75 = 75%
48      64 )48.00
__  =       44 8
64          ____
             3 20
             3 20
             ____
                0
```

1. Practice these examples.

   A. What percent is 30 out of 90?   _____

   B. What percent is 60 out of 240?   _____

   C. What percent is 80 out of 240?   _____

Type 2:

$$\frac{\text{Part}}{\text{Whole}} = \text{Percent} \qquad\qquad \text{Part} = \text{percent times the whole}$$

Bill was going to run 26 miles. He said he would rest after he had run 75% of the distance. How far will he run before he stops?

$$
\begin{array}{r}
26 \\
\times .75 \\
\hline
130 \\
182 \\
\hline
19.50 = 19.5 \text{ miles}
\end{array}
$$

2. Practice these examples.

    A. What is 40% of 180? _____

    B. What is 80% of 240? _____

    C. What is 95% of 36? _____

Type 3:

$$\frac{\text{Part}}{\text{Whole}} = \% \qquad\qquad \frac{\text{Part}}{\text{Percent}} = \text{Whole}$$

Sue knew that when she had hoed 24 of the tomato plants in her garden she was 75% finished. How many tomato plants does she have?

$$24 \div .75 = \text{whole}$$

$$
\begin{array}{r}
32. \\
.75\overline{)24.00} \quad\quad 32 \text{ plants in all} \\
22\ 5 \\
\hline
1\ 50 \\
1\ 50 \\
\hline
0
\end{array}
$$

3. Practice these examples.

    A. 12 is 75% of _____ .

B. 24 is 50% of _____ .

C. 150 is 250% of _____ .

VOCABULARY MATCHING (Answers on page 237.)

1. Ratio	_____	**A.** A punctuation sign used in ratio problems and read "to."
2. Equation	_____	**B.** The quotient of the part divided by the whole.
3. Proportion	_____	
4. Colon	_____	**C.** The "backward" way of doing an operation.
5. Percent	_____	**D.** The answer to a division problem.
6. Quotient	_____	**E.** A statement of equality.
7. Product	_____	**F.** Comparing two ratios.
8. Inverse	_____	**G.** Comparing two numbers by division.
		H. The answer to a multiplication problem.

CUMULATIVE QUIZ (Answers on page 237.)

1. Solve these type 1 percent problems. Express answers as percents.

A. $24 \div 96 =$ _____   **B.** $44 \div 132 =$ _____

C. $14 \div 126 =$ _____   **D.** $\frac{2}{3} \div .50 =$ _____

E. $48 \div .75 =$ _____   **F.** $19 \div 95 =$ _____

2. Solve these type 2 percentage problems.

A. $18 \times 33\frac{1}{3}\% =$ _____   **B.** $2.4 \times 15\% =$ _____

C. $26.5 \times 20\% =$ _____   **D.** $80 \times 64\% =$ _____

E. $63 \times 11\% =$ _____   **F.** $96 \times 4\% =$ _____

3. Solve these type 3 percentage problems.

    A. $12 \div 25\% =$ _____   **B.** $125 \div 50\% =$ _____

    C. $56 \div 8\% =$ _____   **D.** $125 \div .50\% =$ _____

    E. $27 \div 30\% =$ _____   **F.** $64 \div 12\frac{1}{2}\% =$ _____

4. What percent of 90 is 3 more than 50% of 48?

5. When Todd is 40, his son will be 37.5% of his age. That will be 10 years from now. How old is Todd's son now?

6. If Bill works 25 years at the shop, he can retire at 75% of his present salary. If he now makes $12,000.00 a year, what will be his retirement salary?

7. Sue collects porcelain figurines. She thinks that the display case she keeps them in will hold 160 figures. If she already has 140 of them, what percent full is the case?

8. Bill worked on the carburetor of his car. He was getting 22 miles per gallon before. Now he gets $27\frac{1}{2}$ miles per gallon. What percent of **improvement** is that?

9. Martha bought a couch on sale for $250.00. The original price was $300.00. What was the percent of the original price that she paid? What was her percent of savings?

10. David said he had spent 40% of his life teaching. If he has been a teacher for 12 years now, how old is he?

My score on the Cumulative Quiz _____ (number right)

EXTENDING YOUR UNDERSTANDING (Answers on page 238.)

Percent, as it has been defined in these programs, is a fraction with a denominator of 100. If that is true (and it is) then percents fit in the fraction family at the point where the denominator is 100.

Example: $\dfrac{1}{2} = \dfrac{2}{4} = \dfrac{3}{6}$ . . . . $\dfrac{50}{100} = .50 = 50\%$

Because of this relationship they are also proportion problems with one side always having a denominator of 100.

Example: $\dfrac{\text{Part}}{\text{Whole}} = \dfrac{24}{36} = \dfrac{N}{100}$

$24 \times 100 = 2400$
$36 \times N = 36N$
$2400 \div 36 = 66\dfrac{2}{3}$

$N = 66\dfrac{2}{3}$

$\dfrac{66\dfrac{2}{3}}{100} = .66\dfrac{2}{3} = 66\dfrac{2}{3}\%$

Go back to sections 1, 2, and 3 of the cumulative quiz, and see if you can set these examples up so they solve like proportion problems. (Be sure you put the elements in the right place in the proportion problem.)

STEVE WISE SAYS:

1. The basic formula for percent looks like this:

    $$\frac{\text{Part}}{\text{Whole}} = \text{Percent}$$

2. There are three types of percentage problems.

    A. $\dfrac{\text{Part}}{\text{Whole}} = \text{Percent}$

    Example: 10 is what percent of 40?

    $$\frac{10}{40} = .25 = 25\%$$

    B. Part = Percent × Whole

    Example: What is 25% of 40?

    40 × .25 = 10

    C. Whole = Part ÷ Percent

    Example: 25% of what number is 10?

    10 ÷ .25 = 40

3. Each of these types can be derived from the basic formula by using the inverse operation process for simplifying equations.

CHAPTER TEN:
The Percentage Revolution

1 PREVIEW

In this program, we are introduced to a whirlwind of uses for all the things we've learned.

Bill is upset at the way his property tax is figured. He's unfamiliar with the terms used on his tax form. Once he understands them he finds that the way property taxes are figured is very much like percentage problems.

Martha is considering borrowing some money to remodel her family room. She gets involved in the computation of interest, and learns some of the pitfalls of borrowing money.

In the last scene, Todd and Martha are preparing for a sale in Todd's paint store. Martha learns several terms new to her, but she feels right at home with the mathematics because they are applications of what she has learned in her adult math class.

Important Vocabulary

Assessed Evaluation (Value) — Property taxes, in most parts of the country, are figured from value set by the taxing unit of government. This value is established in some way from the actual value of the property.

Cost Price — This is the amount stores pay for the items they sell.

Discount — Often stores sell things for less than the actual selling price. The difference between the sale price and the selling price is the discount.

Discount Rate — The percent of the selling price that is subtracted to get the discount price.

Gross Profit — The simple difference between the cost price and the selling price. Gross profit is usually thought of as the same as mark-up.

Interest — Interest is money that money makes. If you borrow money, you pay a percent of what you borrow for the privilege of using the money. If you have a savings account, you earn interest.

Margin — Same as mark-up or gross profit.

Market Value — This is the actual value of a property, the value it would sell for.

Mark-up — This is the amount stores add to the cost price to get the selling price. Cost price plus mark-up equals selling price.

Mark-up Rate — The percent of the cost price that stores add to the cost to get the selling price.

Principal — The amount you borrow or the amount on which interest is paid or earned.

Profit — After all other expenses are subtracted from the gross profit, what is left is the real profit.

Rate — This means percent. In this program it is used as percent over a certain period of time.

Selling Price — The price you pay for things in a store.

Taxable Amount — The amount you pay taxes on.

Time — In working with interest, the time of the loan is important. Your loan may be for 12% per year. Time for interest problems is usually expressed in years or fractional parts of a year.

2 GOAL SETTING EXERCISE (Answers on page 239.)

1. Express each of the following times as a fractional part of a year. (A month is 30 days.)

   A. 2 months = _____   **B.** 5 months = _____

   C. 10 months = _____   **D.** 9 months, 15 days = _____

   E. 14 months = _____   **F.** 18 months = _____

2. A store is having a 30% discount sale on all merchandise. What is the sale price on the selling prices listed below?

   A. $90.00 _____   **B.** $37.50 _____

   C. $251.80 _____   **D.** $45.85 _____

   E. $75.00 _____   **F.** $65.00 _____

3. Property taxes are figured on so much per hundred dollars of assessed evaluation. How many **hundreds** are there in the following amounts?

   A. $35,000.00 _____   **B.** $9,500.00 _____

   C. $144,500.00 _____   **D.** $28,650.00 _____

4. A drug store got in some new stock. It was to be marked up 42%. What was the selling price on these items?

Cost Price	Selling Price
A. $2.00	_____
B. $3.50	_____
C. $7.70	_____
D. $10.20	_____
E. $15.75	_____

5. Todd borrowed $500.00 at 10% interest for one year. If the principal and the interest were to be paid back in 12 equal payments, how much did he pay each month?

6. Sue started a savings account with $800.00. The bank pays her $5\frac{1}{2}$% per year. How much interest will she collect at the end of 12 months?

7. Bill can borrow money from the credit union where he works at 12% per year. He has a savings account there, too, and they pay him 5% per year. He's thinking about borrowing $1,000.00, and then depositing it in his savings account. Would he make money or lose money this way? How much?

8. What would the total interest be on $3,000.00 at 10% per year for 3 years?

GOAL PROFILE

Put a check mark in the box that fits your situation.

When You Watch the Program

☐ A. If you got them all right,
you're definitely a winner!

Enjoy the program. See if you can figure out Todd's shortcut to finding selling price from cost price in one step.

☐ B. If you missed any part of
number 1, then ....

Review Chapter Three. Concentrate on Martha and her computer.

☐ C. If you missed any part of
number 2, then ....

Review Chapter Nine. Study the sales card that Todd and Martha use in the third scene.

☐ D. If you missed any part of
number 3, then ....

Review Chapter Eight. How does Martha tell Jenny to divide by 100?

☐ E. If you missed any part of
number 4, then ....

Review Chapter Seven. Did you miss them because you figured only the mark-up and failed to add it to the cost price? Todd talks of a short cut to make sure you do it automatically.

☐ F. If you missed number 5,
then ....

Be alert as Martha learns what all these terms mean.

☐ G. If you missed number 6,
then ....

Review Chapter Seven. Study along with Martha.

☐ H. If you missed number 7,
then ....

Review Chapter Seven. David has some clues about this one.

☐ I. If you missed number 8,
then ....

Listen to what Martha has to say about how time affects interest.

3 **NOW YOU ARE READY TO WATCH THE PROGRAM, "THE PERCENTAGE REVOLUTION."**

4 REACT, PRACTICE, AND EXTEND. (Answers on page 239.)

Tips And Short Cuts

Since the three scenes in this program are so different, let's look at each one separately.

Scene 1:

Bill was concerned about the value of his house.

Assessed evaluation — $35,000.00   Evaluation rate — 70%

These are the two numbers Todd used to explain the system to Bill.

Rate of assessment

```
                        500 00.    ← Market value
               .70 ) 35000.00      ← Assessed value
                     350
                      00
```

Then he had to find out how many hundreds are in $35,000.00.

$35,000.00

By moving the decimal point two places to the left (dividing by 100) he got 350 hundreds.

```
     350   ← number of hundreds
   7.25    ← rate per hundred
   1750
    700
   2450
 2537.50   ← base tax
```

Note: The reason local governments use this or similar systems of assigning an assessed evaluation amount to the property is because it is more stable. Market values change all the time, so there would be no way governments could anticipate their income.

The system started at a time when most of our country was farmland. It worked well in those days, but many agree that now it does seem a little clumsy.

1. Figure the property tax on the following properties.

Assessed Value	Rate per Hundred	Tax
A. $5,000.00	$6.15	_____
B. $25,000.00	$1.79	_____
C. $155,000.00	$2.56	_____
D. $24,500.00	$7.80	_____

2. What is the approximate assessed value of these properties according to their market values and assessment rates?

Market Value	Assessment Rate	Assessed Value
A. $90,000.00	60%	_____
B. $62,000.00	55%	_____
C. $16,500.00	71%	_____
D. $20,500.00	57%	_____

Scene 2:

The important thing to learn from this scene is the way percent and time go together to find interest.

$500 at 10% per year for 3 years

Interest = Principal × the Rate × the Time

I = PRT

```
      500   ← Principal
    ×.10    ← Rate
    50.00
      ×3    ← Time
   150.00   ← Interest
```

A very common system for solving problems like this is to write them as a fraction.

$$\frac{500}{1} \times \frac{10}{100} \times \frac{3}{1} \quad \text{reduce the fraction} \quad \frac{\overset{5}{\cancel{500}}}{1} \times \frac{10}{\underset{1}{\cancel{100}}} \times \frac{3}{1} = 150$$

Notice the way Martha got rid of the fractional percent.

$800 at 7.5% for 8 months

Write the problem like this:

$$\frac{800}{1} \times \frac{7.5}{100} \times \frac{2}{3} = \frac{800}{1} \times \underbrace{\frac{15}{200}} \times \frac{2}{3}$$

$$8 \text{ months} = \frac{8}{12} = \frac{2}{3} \qquad \Big\uparrow$$

By using this member of the fraction family, Martha did away with the decimal fraction.

Reduce the fraction for the answer.

$$\frac{\overset{4}{\cancel{800}}}{1} \times \frac{\overset{5}{\cancel{15}}}{\underset{1}{\cancel{200}}} \times \frac{2}{\underset{1}{\cancel{3}}} = \frac{40}{1} = \$40.00$$

3. Use this fractional way of solving these interest problems.

   A. $2,500.00 at 15% for 2 years.

   B. $18,000.00 at 14.5% for 20 years.

   C. $200.00 at 22% for 6 months.

   D. $500 at 15% for $1\frac{1}{2}$ years.

Scene 3:

Here is the process Todd and Martha used to fill out the sales card:

Cost price × mark-up rate = mark-up

Cost price + mark-up = selling price

Selling price × discount rate = discount

Selling price − discount = sale price

Example: Cost = $6.00   Mark-up = $3.00   Everything else can be computed from here if you remember that Todd said that the sale price must not be **less** than the cost price.

$$\frac{3.00}{6.00} = 6.00\overline{)3.00.00}^{\;.50\,=\,50\%} \quad \text{mark-up rate}$$

$$6.00 + 3.00 = \$9.00 \quad \text{selling price}$$

$$9.00 \times 30\% = \$2.70$$

$$9.00 - 2.70 = \$6.30$$

4. Complete the chart below with the information given. (The "lot number" is just for identification purposes in the stock room.)

LOT NO.	COST PRICE	MARK UP	MARK-UP RATE	SELLING PRICE	DISCOUNT RATE	SALE PRICE
A.	6.00	3.00	50%	9.00	30%	_____
B.	_____	3.64	_____	10.64	30%	_____
C.	9.30	4.46	_____	_____	30%	_____
D.	_____	_____	46%	16.79	30%	_____
E.	10.20	5.51	_____	_____	30%	_____

CUMULATIVE QUIZ (Answers on page 240.)

1. Work these decimal fraction problems.

A. $2.4 \times 3.8 =$ _____   B. $2.63 \div 4.2 =$ _____

C. $44.7 \times .35 =$ _____   D. $2.08 \div .35 =$ _____

E. $6.2 \times 4.3 =$ _____   F. $7.7 \div 1.23 =$ _____

2. Simplify these ratio problems.

A. $\dfrac{13}{39}$ = _____

B. $\dfrac{7}{4}$ = _____

C. $\dfrac{18}{6}$ = _____

D. $\dfrac{\frac{2}{3}}{\frac{3}{4}}$ = _____

E. $\dfrac{26}{5}$ = _____

F. $\dfrac{2\frac{3}{8}}{4}$ = _____

Before you complete the Cumulative Quiz, take a little time to look at Todd's short cut for finding the selling price when cost and mark-up rate are known. He told Martha how to do it, but you may have missed it.

The plan for finding the selling price is as follows:

Cost × Mark-up Rate = Mark-up

$6.00 × 50% = $3.00

Mark-up + Cost = Selling Price

$3.00 + $6.00 = $9.00

But you can do it in one step if you don't necessarily need to know the mark-up. You can add **before** you multiply. By adding 100% to the mark-up rate, you can go directly from cost price to selling price.

Cost × (Mark-up Rate + 100%) = Selling Price

$6.00 × 150% = $9.00

The reason this works is the 100% stands for 100% of the cost price. The cost price is in the computation from the very beginning, and doesn't need to be added afterward.

It works the other way, too.

Selling Price ÷ (Mark-up Rate + 100%) = Cost

$9.00 ÷ 150% = $6.00

Tips and Short Cuts

It is good to remember that a discount of 30% means that you will be paying 70% of the selling price. This gives you two ways to find the sale price when you know the discount rate.

Selling Price =	$27.00	$27.00		100%	$27.00
Discount Rate =	× .30	− 8.10	or	− 30%	× .70
Discount =	$8.10	$18.90		70%	$18.90

Now go on with the Cumulative Quiz.

3.   Solve these proportion problems.

    A. $\dfrac{3}{7} = \dfrac{N}{21}$ **B.** $\dfrac{4}{3.8} = \dfrac{N}{15}$

    C. $\dfrac{3}{14} = \dfrac{16}{N}$ **D.** $\dfrac{2}{.34} = \dfrac{7}{N}$

4.   Solve these percent problems.

    A. 45% of 28 = _____   **B.** 77% of N = 68.53

    C. 33.5% of 77 = _____   **D.** 46% of N = 21.16

5.   Find the interest in these problems.

    A. $200.00 at 12% for 1 year

    B. $250.00 at 18% for 4 months

    C. $700.00 at $5\frac{1}{2}$% for 2 years

    D. $2,500.00 at 8% for $3\frac{1}{2}$ years

6. Solve these discount problems.

	Selling Price	Discount Rate	Sale Price
A.	$ 54.00	30%	_____
B.	$125.00	20%	_____
C.	$145.00	45%	_____

7. Martha was going to buy a table that was on sale at a 35% discount. The clerk told her that if she would come back tomorrow, the table would be on sale at 40% and she would save $5.00 more. What was the selling price of the table?

8. In 3 days Todd sold $1,200.00 worth of paint. At that rate, how much could you expect him to sell in 20 days?

9. What is the interest for 3 years on a 14% loan of $1,200.00? (simple interest)

10. Frank wants to put enough into a savings account so that he will get $300.00 in interest each year. If the savings account is at 8%, how much will he need to deposit?

Cumulative Quiz score _____ (number right)

EXTENDING YOUR UNDERSTANDING (Answers on page 241.)

1. A man bought a horse for $100.00, and sold it for $200.00. He bought back the same horse for $300.00, and sold it again for $400.00. He bought the horse one more time for $500.00, and sold it this time for $600.00. Did he make money, lose money, or break even?

Compound interest is interest that interest makes. Savings accounts are most affected by compound interest. Interest that is earned in one term is added to the principal, and interest for the next term is computed on the total amount during the next period. In savings accounts the term can be annual (yearly), semi-annual (half-year), quarterly, monthly, or even daily.

After the interest is added to the principal, it is called the "amount (A)."

Example: Sue had a savings account of $400.00 that paid 5% interest semi-annually. How much money would she have at the end of one year?

$400.00 at 5% semi-annually (twice a year)

After 6 months,

$$\frac{\overset{2}{\overset{4}{\cancel{400}}}}{1} \times \frac{5}{\underset{1}{\cancel{100}}} \times \frac{1}{\underset{1}{\cancel{2}}} = \$10.00$$

This means that in 6 months she will get half the annual interest.

After one year,

$$\frac{\overset{205}{\cancel{410}}}{1} \times \frac{\cancel{5}}{\underset{20}{\cancel{100}}} \times \frac{1}{\underset{1}{2}} = \frac{205}{20} = 10.25 \quad 410 + 10.25 = A$$

Total amount after 1 year = $420.25

How much would she have after 2 years?

After $1\frac{1}{2}$ years,

$$\frac{420.25}{1} \times \frac{\overset{1}{\cancel{5}}}{\underset{20}{\cancel{100}}} \times \frac{1}{2} = \frac{420.25}{40} = 10.51$$

$420.25 + 10.51 = A$

After 2 years,

$$\frac{430.76}{1} \times \frac{\overset{1}{\cancel{5}}}{\underset{20}{\cancel{100}}} \times \frac{1}{2} = \frac{430.76}{40} = 10.77 \quad 430.76 + 10.77 = A$$

Total amount after 2 years = $441.53

Notice that "semi-annual" means that in 2 years there are 4 terms. "Quarterly" would mean 8 terms in 2 years, and 8 computations are necessary.

Compute the compound interest on these examples.

2. Find the amount (A) for $1,500.00 at 4% compounded quarterly for 2 years.

3. Find the amount (A) for $2,500.00 at 8% compounded annually for 6 years.

STEVE WISE SAYS:

1. Interest is money that is made or paid on other money.

2. If you get a loan, you pay interest.

3. If you have a savings account, you receive interest.

4. The formula for finding interest is I = PRT. Interest is equal to principal times the rate (or percent) times the time.

CHAPTER ELEVEN:
Being Positive About Signed Numbers

1 PREVIEW

Most people suppose that signed numbers, especially numbers that are signed negative, are reserved for some mathematical or scientific world that is foreign to the average person.

Not true.

In the first scene, you will see and hear some fairly common-sounding conversation, but within what the people say, all the operations involving signed numbers are used.

In scene two, you will learn the formal rules governing calculations involving signed numbers.

Scene three starts getting you in the swing of thinking algebraically, the real reason for studying signed numbers.

Important Vocabulary

Absolute Value — Every number has two parts. One of the parts is the plus or minus sign that indicates whether it is a positive or negative number. This part tells you which way from zero the number is on the number line. The second part is the numerical part that describes the "bigness" or distance from zero. This numerical part is called the absolute value. +4 and −4 both have an absolute value of 4.

Equal — In algebra, this is the balance point in a number statement. 2 + 2 = 4 is an equation because it has the same amount on each side. **Equations must always balance.**

Equation — In mathematics, any statement that includes an equal sign is an equation; hence, 2 + 3 = 5 is an equation, since the same amount is on both sides. Likewise A + B = C is an equation and A + B is the same as C, whatever they are.

Infinity — This is where numbers end. This is only an idea, since for our purposes, there is no such place. Now that we are dealing with negative numbers, too, infinity extends both ways from zero.

Inverse Operations — In mathematics, for every way of doing something, there is a way to "undo" it. You undo addition by subtraction, multiplication by division, and so forth. By using inverse operations, algebraic expressions can be simplified.

Minus — The minus sign (−) in algebra is used to tell two things. It tells of the operation of subtraction. It also tells which direction from zero a number lies on the number line. In algebra, subtraction is generally thought of as addition of a negative number.

Negative Numbers — Numbers which express a value less than zero are called negative numbers. Imagine that you have $5, that's positive $5. If you buy something that costs $10, you are $5 in the hole (negative) $(5 - 10 = -5)$.

Number Line — This is a picture of our number system. Such a line exists only in our imagination. For this program, the number line starts at zero and extends both directions.

Number Sign — In this program, this term is used to differentiate between the signed number and the operation of addition and subtraction.

Opposite of — In some math books, negative numbers are treated as if they are the opposite of positive numbers. In those systems, −8 is read, "The opposite of 8" and −(−8) is read, "The opposite of the opposite of 8" and so forth.

Plus — The plus sign (+) tells you to add. Like the minus sign, it is that part of a number that tells which direction a number is from zero.

Positive Numbers — In signed numbers, zero is the starting place or "origin." Those numbers which are more than zero are positive.

Positive Totals/Negative Totals — In solving addition or subtraction problems where there is a series of several negative and positive numbers, you will be asked to get a total of all the positive and a total of all the negative numbers and to compare these totals.

Real Number — Any number used to describe the distance from zero is a real number. Real numbers can be either negative or positive.

Signed Numbers — Numbers that include a sign (plus or minus) as a part of the quantity they express are called signed numbers. All numbers have such signs, but because we usually work with the positive ones, we don't usually write the sign. Therefore, a number that does not have a sign connected with it is considered to be positive. The number, −4, is such a signed number and is read "minus four" in this TV series.

Simplify — As the term is used in this program, it means to rewrite a numerical statement of equality as simply as possible. It is often said that the main idea of algebra is to get all the unknowns on one side of the equal sign and all the numbers on the other. For our purposes here, that is what we are trying to do.

Substitution — It is often advantageous to call a quantity by an equivalent name to simplify a mathematical statement. Calling $\frac{1}{2}$ "$\frac{2}{4}$" is a form of substitution. There are times when a problem can be solved more easily if a letter is substituted for a value and vice-versa.

Unequal — Often it is as important to show that things are unequal as it is to show that they are equal. There is a sign to use in this case. $\neq$ means "is not equal." $7 + 3 \neq 12$.

Zero — This is the most important number when considering signed numbers. It is neither negative nor positive, yet **it is** a counting number. Unless you live in a zoo, zero probably counts the number of elephants that are in the room where you're sitting at this moment.

2 GOAL SETTING EXERCISE (Answers on page 242.)

Solve these sets of exercises.

1. On the number line below, write the numbers that are indicated by the letters.

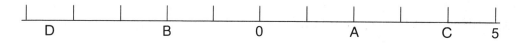

2. Subtract the following examples.

   A. 12 minus 8   **B.** 8 minus 12

   C. $(8-12) + (3-7)$ **D.** $(6-15) - (15-6)$

3. What is the difference between:

   A. 40° above zero and 12° below zero?
   B. 4° below zero and 14° above?
   C. 4° below zero and 68° above?
   D. 8° below zero and 2° below zero?

4. Bill's pay check was $440. He spent $200 for rent, $175 for food, his brother gave him $20 he owed him, and he spent $35 to get his car fixed. How much money does Bill have left, if any?

5. Fill in the missing numbers.

   A. 4   **B.** 8   **C.** 9   **D.** −14

   $$4 - \Box = 10 \qquad 8 + \Box = 6 \qquad 9 + \Box = 18 \qquad -14 + \Box = -6$$

6. Do the following multiplication or division problems.

A. +6 times +6 = _____

B. −4 times −4 = _____

C. +8 times −3 = _____

D. −5 times −5 = _____

E. 15 ÷ 3 = _____

F. −20 ÷ 5 = _____

G. −6 $\overline{)\ 36}$ = _____

H. −5 $\overline{)\ -25}$ = _____

I. −12 $\overline{)\ -3}$ = _____

7. Fill in the missing numbers.

A. $+3 \times \boxed{} = 21$

B. $+3 \times \boxed{} = -21$

C. $-3 \times \boxed{} = 21$

D. $-3 \times \boxed{} = -21$

8. What numbers make these equations balance?

A. $7 + N = 12$ N = _____

B. $2 \cdot W = 14$ W = _____

C. $2N - 5 = 12 + N$ N = _____

D. $\dfrac{4Q}{2} = 17 - 12$ Q = _____

9. Fill in the missing numbers.

A. $3 + \boxed{} = -6$

B. $4 \times \boxed{} = 16$

C. $\boxed{} \div -3 = 9$

D. $4 + \boxed{} + 3 - 2 = -5$

10. If Todd had 20 gallons of paint on a particular shelf and every day he took away 4 gallons, and if he noticed on Saturday he was taking away the last 4 cans, when did he start taking them off?

GOAL PROFILE

Put a check in the box that fits your situation.

When You Watch the Program

☐ A. If you got all of them right, ...
Wonderful! But it's still a good idea to pay attention to the rules for addition and subtraction of signed numbers.

☐ B. If you missed any part of number 1, then . . . .
Frank explains how number lines are used to understand negative numbers.

☐ C. If you missed any part of number 2, then . . . .
The rules for addition and subtraction are in scene two. Better watch them closely.

☐ D. If you missed any part of number 3, then . . . .
A thermometer is a number line of sorts. Listen to what Sue has to say about thermometers.

☐ E. If you missed any part of number 4, then . . . .
Listen carefully to the discussion in scene two about income and expenses.

☐ F. If you missed any part of number 5, then . . . .
Pay particular attention to the rules for addition.

☐ G. If you missed any part of number 6, then . . . .
You need to know more about the rules for multiplication and division of signed numbers.

☐ H. If you missed any part of numbers 8 or 9, then . . . .
Pay particular attention to scene three.

☐   I.   If you missed any part of
number 10, then . . . .   This is a division of a negative number
problem. Be certain you catch this in
the program.

3 NOW YOU ARE READY TO WATCH THE PROGRAM, "BEING POSITIVE ABOUT SIGNED NUMBERS."

4 REACT, PRACTICE AND EXTEND. (Answers on page 243.)

1. Here are some examples similar to those in the program. Can you solve them?

   A. $(-5) + (+10) = $ _____

   B. $(-5) + $ ☐ $ = +10$

   C. $(-12) + (+16) = $ _____

2. Here is a balance sheet for a small business.

	INCOME	EXPENSES
Monday	$ 80.75	$23.80
Tuesday	$ 46.50	$96.00
Wednesday	$153.00	$14.00
Thursday	$226.00	$17.00
Friday	$ 53.00	$68.00

   During the week, did this business make money or lose money? How much?

3. Try these addition problems.

   A. $\begin{array}{r} 14 \\ +(-6) \\ \hline \end{array}$ B. $\begin{array}{r} -36 \\ +(+6) \\ \hline \end{array}$

   C. $\begin{array}{r} 25 \\ +(-5) \\ \hline \end{array}$ D. $\begin{array}{r} +15 \\ +(+7) \\ \hline \end{array}$

4. Try these subtraction problems.

   A. $\begin{array}{r} +14 \\ -(+7) \\ \hline \end{array}$ B. $\begin{array}{r} -26 \\ -(+8) \\ \hline \end{array}$

   C. $\begin{array}{r} -32 \\ -(-8) \\ \hline \end{array}$ D. $\begin{array}{r} -8 \\ -(+48) \\ \hline \end{array}$

5. Solve these multiplication problems.

    A. $(+25) \times (+5) = $ _____

    B. $(-12) \times (-6) = $ _____

    C. $(+5) \times (-7) = $ _____

    D. $(-8) \times (+4) = $ _____

6. Solve these division problems.

    A. $(+18) \div (+6) = $ _____

    B. $(-16) \div (-4) = $ _____

    C. $(-10) \div (+5) = $ _____

    D. $(+44) \div (-11) = $ _____

7. Simplify these equations by inverse operations.

    A. $3 + N = 17$ $N = $ _____

    B. $7 - W = 4$ $W = $ _____

    C. $3Q = 15$ $Q = $ _____

    D. $\dfrac{Z}{4} = \dfrac{16}{2}$ $Z = $ _____

8. If $A = 4$, $B = 5$ and $Q = 9$, solve the following substitution problems.

    A. $B - Q = $ _____

    B. $\dfrac{A + B}{Q} = $ _____

    C. $2A - B = $ _____

    D. $2A + 3B - Q = $ _____

VOCABULARY MATCHING (Answers on page 243.)

1. Absolute value   _____

2. Infinity   _____

3. Positive number   _____

4. Negative number   _____

5. Zero   _____

A. Mythical end to numbers.

B. The number that tells the distance from zero.

C. The only number that is neither negative nor positive.

D. A number less than zero.

E. A number greater than zero.

RULES AND EXAMPLES

The most important part of dealing with signed numbers is a good understanding of the rules for addition. They seem complex but they are logically explained.

We'll take each rule apart and give examples of how it works.

1.   If the signs are the same, add and use the sign in the answer.

Examples:

$$\begin{array}{r} (+4) \\ + (+4) \\ \hline +8 \end{array}$$

You've done this forever.

$$\begin{array}{r} (-5) \\ + (-10) \\ \hline -15 \end{array}$$

Adding a negative to a negative makes it **more** negative.

2.   If the signs are different, subtract* and use the number sign of the larger number for the answer.

Examples:

$$\begin{array}{r} (+12) \\ + (-4) \\ \hline \end{array} \qquad \begin{array}{r} 12 \\ - 4 \\ \hline 8 \end{array} = +8$$

(12 is larger and positive, use "+" in answer.)

*Adding a negative to a positive is like subtraction.

$$\begin{array}{r} (+3) \\ + (-12) \\ \hline \end{array} \qquad \begin{array}{r} 12 \\ - 3 \\ \hline \end{array}$$

If you're adding one positive and one negative, just subtract whichever way seems natural and use the sign of the larger number for the answer.

RULES FOR ADDING MORE THAN TWO SIGNED NUMBERS.

1. Make a total of the positive numbers.

2. Make a total of the negative numbers.

3. Subtract the smaller total from the larger total and give the answer the sign of the larger total.

Example:

$(-3) + (-4) + (+5) + (+6) + (-2)$

Positive Total $5 + 6 = 11$ $(+11)$

Negative Total $3 + 4 + 2 = 9$ $\underline{+ (-9)}$

$+2$

ADDITION PRACTICE EXAMPLES (Answers on page 244.)

1. $(+6) + (-8) = $ _____

2. $(+3) + (-2) = $ _____

3. $(-12) + (-4) = $ _____

4. $(-4) + (+16) = $ _____

RULES FOR SUBTRACTION OF SIGNED NUMBERS

This rule is the most perplexing and often the hardest to remember.

1. Change the sign of the number being subtracted to the opposite one.

2. Use the rules for addition of signed numbers.

Example:		Add	
	-14	-14	The logic is a little hazy on problems like this. This would
	$\underline{- (+9)}$	$\underline{- 9}$	be like having a $14 debt and
		-23	**not** getting $9 you expected. In effect, you are $23 in the hole.

Example:		Add	
	$+12$	$+12$	You might think of it this way. If you had $12 and you somehow
	$\underline{- (-6)}$	$\underline{+6}$	subtracted a debt of $6, the effect
		$+18$	is the same as if you had $18.

SUBTRACTION PRACTICE (Answers on page 244.)

1. $(-10) - (-6) =$ _____

2. $(+14) - (-3) =$ _____

3. $(+17) - (+8) =$ _____

4. $(-4) - (+16) =$ _____

RULES FOR MULTIPLICATION OF SIGNED NUMBERS

1. If the number signs are the same, multiply and give the answer a positive sign.

2. If the signs are different, multiply and give the answer a negative sign.

A. $(+4) \times (+4) = +16$

C. $(-5) \times (+5) = -25$

B. $(-6) \times (-6) = +36$

D. $(+3) \times (-3) = -9$

Usually this is easy to remember. Yet, if you have trouble, think of this story.

You want to go out to eat. That's a positive situation.

Your friend wants to go out to eat, too. That's a positive situation, also. You can bet you will have a positive evening.

One evening you **don't** want to go out. That's a negative. Your friend **doesn't** want to go out, either. That's negative, too. You will still have a positive evening because you agree on a negative point.

Now suppose you want to go out to eat (positive), but your friend doesn't (negative).

You're bound to have a **negative** evening.

MULTIPLICATION PRACTICE (Answers on page 244.)

1. $(+6) \times (+7) =$ _____

2. $(-4) \times (-5) =$ _____

3. $(-8) \times (+6) =$ _____

4. $(+9) \times (-5) =$ _____

RULE FOR DIVISION OF SIGNED NUMBERS

The rule for division is the same as the rule for multiplication.

Examples:

$(+15) \div (+5) = +3$

$(-15) \div (+5) = -3$

DIVISION PRACTICE (Answers on page 244.)

1. $(+24) \div (-3) =$ _____

2. $(-6) \div (-2) =$ _____

3. $(+12) \div (+4) =$ _____

4. $(-3) \div (+5) =$ _____

BALANCE IN ALGEBRA

The purpose of using a balance scale in the video portion of the program was to demonstrate the nature of equality in an algebra statement.

The technique of inverse operations was used to simplify the expression. If you paid close attention, you noticed the final answer had the unknown (the letter) on one side of the equal sign and the numbers on the other.

You may want to think of "GARBAGE" to accomplish this.

Example:

$Q + 4 = 16$

Garbage

"Garbage" is a number on the side of the equation where you want to collect the letters, or a letter on the side where you want the numbers to be. The "garbage" can be removed by inverse operations.

The inverse of addition is subtraction.

$$
\begin{array}{rr}
Q + 4 = & 16 \\
-4 & -4 \\
\hline
Q + 0 = & 12
\end{array}
$$
Garbage is gone.

Try another one:

Example: $3W - 8 = 24 - W$ (Garbage)

Inverse

$$
\begin{array}{rr}
+8 & +8 \quad W \\
\hline
3W & = 32 - W
\end{array}
$$

Inverse

$$
\begin{array}{rr}
+W & = \quad +W \\
\hline
4W & = 32
\end{array}
$$

The 4 is garbage in this next example.

Inverse of multiplication is division.

$$\frac{\cancel{4}W}{\cancel{4}} = \frac{\overset{8}{\cancel{32}}}{\cancel{4}}$$

$$W = 8 \qquad \text{All garbage is gone.}$$

PRACTICE (Answers on page 244.)

Get the "garbage" out of these expressions.

1. $3W + 7 = 25$ W =

2. $P + 7 = 3$ P =

3. $4X + 9 = X - 3$ X =

4. $12 - Z = 5$ Z =

CUMULATIVE QUIZ (Answers on page 244.)

1. Add the following examples.

   A. $(+4) + (+7) = $ _____

   B. $(-7) + (-7) = $ _____

   C. $(+9) + (-12) = $ _____

   D. $(+10) + (-12) + (+3) = $ _____

2. Subtract the following examples.

   A. $(+4) - (+3) = $ _____   B. $(-2) - (+17) = $ _____

   C. $(+7) - (-8) = $ _____   D. $(+7) - (-7) = $ _____

3. Multiply these examples.

   A. $(+27) \times (-3) = $ _____

   B. $(+15) \times (+12) = $ _____

   C. $(-7) \times (-7) =$ _____

   D. $(-5) \times (+5) =$ _____

4. Divide these examples.

   A. $(+18) \div (+6) =$ _____   **B.** $(-36) \div (-6) =$ _____

   C. $(+24) \div (-6) =$ _____   **D.** $(-5) \div (-15) =$ _____

5. Fill in the blanks.

   A. $(-5) -$ _____ $= (-15)$ **B.** _____ $\div (+6) = (-12)$

   C. $(+20) -$ _____ $= (+25)$ **D.** _____ $\times (-4) = (+16)$

6. In the words of a popular song Roger Miller sang a few years back, "I lack $14 of having 57¢." How much money did he have?

7. Todd and some friends were playing pinochle. The first hand Todd and his partner made 28 points. The second hand they lost 35 points. The third hand they made 17 points and the fourth hand they lost 25 points. What was Todd's score at this point?

8. What is eight more than five less than two?

9. Todd found out that six times during the year the paint store had lost $20 on a particular item that was marked wrong. Express this situation as a problem in multiplication of signed numbers. How much was lost?

   Cumulative score _____ (number right)

EXTENDING YOUR UNDERSTANDING

Some textbooks have a different system for adding signed numbers. Their approach is stated like this.

1. Express the addend with the greater value as some number plus the additive inverse of the other addend.

2. Use the properties of addition to find the sum.

   Example:

   How much of

   this   offsets this?

   ↓   ↗

   +12   +   −25   =   +12 + [(−12) + (−13)] =

   [(+12) + (−12)] + (−13)

   (0) + (−13)

   −13

See if you can use this system to solve the following examples. (Answers on page 245.)

   A. (+9) + (−16)

   B. (−12) + (+6)

   C. (−44) + (+18)

   D. (+16) + (−33)

STEVE WISE SAYS:

RULES FOR ADDING TWO SIGNED NUMBERS:

1. If the number signs are the same, add and use that number sign in the answer.

2. If the number signs are different, subtract and use the sign of the larger number as the number sign in the answer.

RULES FOR SUBTRACTING SIGNED NUMBERS:

1. Change the sign of the number being subtracted to the opposite sign.

2. Use the rules for adding signed numbers.

RULES FOR MULTIPLYING AND DIVIDING SIGNED NUMBERS:

1. If the number signs are the same, the answer is positive.

2. If the number signs are different, the answer is negative.

REMEMBER:
Study these rules.
1. If there are no signs between a number and a letter, it means to multiply.
2. If there are no signs between a letter and a parenthesis, it means to multiply.

CHAPTER TWELVE:

Algebra On The Run

1 PREVIEW

Algebra is the workhorse of mathematics and science. It provides a system for finding solutions that would otherwise be very difficult to come by.

This program deals with those understandings that are the most basic in the study of algebra.

You'll hear more about balance and inverse operations, and about the process of substitution.

Of major importance is the sequence of operations.

In the second scene, the idea of powers and roots is introduced.

Be alert! This is **Algebra On The Run**. The ideas come quickly and can sneak up on you.

After viewing this program and completing the examples in the workbook, you should have a greater appreciation for the intricacies of our number system.

Important Vocabulary

Co-efficient — The number part of an expression is often called the co-efficient. In 3X the 3 is the co-efficient and the X is the variable.

Constant and Variable — It is easier to think of these two terms together. An algebraic expression is often made up of two parts, a number and a letter. The number does not change in value so it is called a constant. The letter can be assigned any value desired. Since it **varies** it is called a variable.

Example: The expression $8N + 4$ has numerical meaning only if we know the value of N. If $N = 2$, then 8N (multiplication is implied if there is no space between the characters) would be 16 and $8N + 4$ would equal 20. If N were something else, the answer would not be 20.

Formula — This is a plan for finding out a specific bit of information. It is a general statement. By substitution of specific values for the variables in a formula, you can get specific answers.

Example: $P = 4S$ is the formula for the perimeter of **all** squares. The perimeter of a square that has sides of six inches would be $P = 4 \times 6$ or 24.

Graph — A graph is a picture that describes more than one idea at a time.

Literal Equation — In algebra, general statements are made by using letters to represent quantities. $C - T = W$ is a literal equation. The numerical value of any one of these variables depends on the value of the other two.

Power — This refers to a number being multiplied by itself. Powers are written with two numbers, the base and the exponent. The base tells the number being considered and the exponent tells how many times it is multiplied by itself.

Example: 2^2 means 2×2 or 4. 2^3 means $2 \times 2 \times 2$ or 8. A number with a power (exponent) of 1 is that number; $4^1 = 4$. A number to the power of zero always equals 1; $16^0 = 1$.

Requested Unknown — In this series you will be asked to solve an equation in terms of other unknowns. In the literal statement, $C - T = W$, you might be asked, "What is T?" In this case, T is the requested unknown. The answer is expressed in terms of the other variables. For instance, $T = C - W$.

Root — This is the opposite of power. If a number is raised to a power, there must be a process to get back to where it started. The most often used root is "square root." 3^2 is read three square and equals 9. Finding the square root of a number answers the question. "What number multiplied by itself equals 9?" The square root of 25 is 5 because $5 \times 5 = 25$.

It is possible to find the root of any power. For example, the cube root of 27 is 3 since $3 \times 3 \times 3$ equals 27.

Sequence of Operations — Mathematicians, by agreement, have decided which of the mathematical operations comes first in a series of operations. For instance, multiplication is handled before addition. So in the number sentence $2 + 4 \times 3$, the answer is 14 (3×4 first, then add 2). If you added first, then multiplied, you'd get 18; and that's not right.

Simultaneous Equations — One way of solving for more than one unknown is to compare two statements of equality for the same relationship of number. When this is done together, the process is called simultaneous solution. There is an example of this process in the video program.

2 GOAL SETTING EXERCISE

Solve these sets of exercises. (Answers on page 246.)

1. Find the missing numbers in these exercises.

    A. $17 + \boxed{} = 21$ B. $14 + \boxed{} = 2$

    C. $\boxed{} + 3 = 8$ D. $3 - \boxed{} = 7$

2. In each case, find the value of N

    A. $N + 6 = 0$ $N = $ _____   **B.** $N \cdot 4 = 0$ $N = $ _____

    C. $2N - 6 = N$ $N = $ _____   **D.** $3N - 2 = 2N + 1$ $N = $ _____

3. In this example, A is always 7 and B is always 4. Fill in the blanks with the right answer.

    A. $2A + 2B = $ _____   **B.** $2A + 1 - 6B + 4 = $ _____

    C. $A \div 2B = $ _____   **D.** $A - 9 + B - 6 = $ _____

4. Write the answers to the following squares.

    A. $8^2 = $ _____   **B.** $25^2 = $ _____

    C. X^2 where $X = 7$ _____   **D.** $0^2 = $ _____

5. Do the following multiplication problems.

    A. $2X \cdot 2 = $ _____   **B.** $2X \cdot 2X = $ _____

    C. $2A \cdot B = $ _____   **D.** $3B^2 \cdot 2 = $ _____

6. Fill in the missing numbers.

    A. $2 + 3 \times 6 = $ _____   **B.** $2 + 4 \div 2 = $ _____

    C. $2 (+ 3) - (2 \times 6) - 2 = $ _____   **D.** $X (3 + 6) = $ _____

7. What are the square roots of these numbers?

    A. 81 _____   **B.** 100 _____

    C. 225 _____   **D.** B^2 _____

8. What number times two plus two is the same as that number times three minus four?

9. Sue spent $5 more than Martha. Together they spent $19. How much did each of them spend?

10. Oranges cost three times as much as pears; pears cost twice as much as apples. How much does one apple cost in terms of oranges?

GOAL PROFILE

Put a check in the box that fits your situation

When You Watch the Program

☐ A. If you got all of them right, ...

Mercy! Still, you may need to refresh your memory of the process of square root.

☐ B. If you missed any part of number 1, ...

This is an inverse operation problem. Watch carefully. It comes up several times in the program.

☐ C. If you missed any part of number 2, ...

More inverse operations. How to use the inverse is one of the major topics of this program. Watch carefully.

☐ D. If you missed any part of number 3, ...

This is an example of substitution. Concentrate on those parts of the program which explain how important this technique is.

☐ E. If you missed any part of number 4, ...

You'll need to refresh your understanding of powers.

☐ F. If you missed any part of number 5, ...

Be sure you follow the part of the program where they talk about powers and roots.

□ G. If you missed any part of
       number 6, ... These problems have to do with
                                     sequence of operations. If you don't
                                     catch it all in the program, there is more
                                     help in the workbook.

□ H. If you missed any part of
       number 7, ... Square root is a necessary skill in
                                     algebra. Be sure you understand the
                                     averaging method operation.

□ I. If you missed any part of
       number 8, ... Listen to Todd and Sue discuss literal
                                     equations.

□ J. If you missed any part of
       number 9, ... This is a substitution problem. It is
                                     important to be able to take a statement
                                     in English and write it in terms of
                                     algebra. More help later on.

□ K. If you missed any part of
       number 10, ... This is a real world example of a literal
                                     equation. The third scene deals with
                                     literal equations.

3 **NOW YOU ARE READY TO WATCH THE PROGRAM,
"ALGEBRA ON THE RUN."**

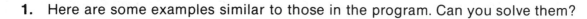

4 **REACT, PRACTICE, AND EXTEND.** (Answers on page 246.)

1. Here are some examples similar to those in the program. Can you solve them?

A. $Q + 5 = 0$ **B.** $3X + 5 = 14$

$Q = $ _____ $X = $ _____

C. $2Y \div 7 = 10$ **D.** $2Z + Y = 19$

$Y = $ _____ $Z + Y = 12$

                         $Z = $ _____ $Y = $ _____

2. Here are some literal equations. Don't let them throw you. Literal means "letters" and the same rules apply to literal equations that apply to numbers. $C = 7$, $E = 9$, $F = 11$.

A. $C + E = $ _____   **B.** $C + EF = $ _____

C. $F - C + E = $ _____   **D.** $C^2 + E = $ _____

3. Let's try a few more examples. $Q = Y + 3$, find Y if . . .

A. $Q = 6$ $Y = $ _____   **B.** $Q = 9$ $Y = $ _____

C. $Q = Z$ $Y = $ _____   **D.** $Q = -4$ $Y = $ _____

Sue and Todd looked at several charts and worksheets. Some of the ideas from the charts and worksheets are explained more fully on the following pages.

Note: See the appendix in this workbook for a complete set of charts.

In Algebra, letters are used to represent numbers.
In you write $X + 8$, the answer depends on the value assigned to X.
If $X = 2$, then $X + 8 = 10$
If $X = 7$, then $X + 8 = 15$

Remember: X is called a variable because its value can change. 8 (or any number part of an expression) is called the constant, because it doesn't change.
This information becomes important when you realize that by **substituting** values for the variables, you can get information you can't easily get any other way.

Let's see how substitution fits the kinds of problems you run into every day.

Example: Bill cut a twenty-foot board into two pieces. The longer one was two feet more than twice the length of the shorter one. How long were both boards?

O.K. Let's make algebra out of the English. Incidentally, there are several ways to translate this statement. The plan used here is a logical, step-by-step approach. As you gain skills, you'll find many shorter ways to write this kind of problem.
Step 1 - Let's call the longer piece X and the shorter piece Y. The story says that $X + Y = 20$.
That means that both pieces together are twenty feet long, the length of the original board.
Step 2 - The story gives some additional information. It says that two times the shorter piece, plus two feet, is the length of the longer one.
In algebra it looks like this, $2Y + 2 = X$.
Step 3 - Here's where we substitute. If $2Y + 2 = X$, **then it can be substituted for X.** $X + Y = 20$ can be written $2Y + 2 + Y = 20$. Got it?
What we have done is express X in terms of Y. It has the effect of getting rid of one unknown (X). Now all we have to worry about is Y.
Step 4 - Simplify the equation.
$2Y + 2 + Y = 20$.
Collect the Y's.
$3Y + 2 = 20$.

Ask, "What number do I have to add to two to get twenty?"
18 of course.
$3Y = 18$
If three of them are 18, then one of them is 6.
$Y = 6$

Now here is the next substitution that needs to be done to get all the numbers figured out. Go back to the first expression we wrote for this story, $X + Y = 20$, and substitute 6 for the Y in this problem. Then we have $X + 6 = 20$.
Ask, "What number must I add to six to get twenty?"
See? $X = 14$.
Now let's check our thinking again by substitution in the original problem.
We **think** $X = 14$ and we **think** $Y = 6$.
$X + Y = 20$. Does $14 + 6 = 20$? Sure does!
But have we taken care of all the information?
Let's check out one more thing. At one point we said that $2Y + 2 + Y = 20$.
Does $2 \times 6 + 2 + 6 = 20$?   Yep!

PRACTICE EXAMPLES (Answers on page 247.)

Here are some practice examples for you to try this process.

1. Bill and his wife went shopping for some canned goods which were on sale. They bought three times as many cans of beans as they did peaches. They bought twice as many cans of tomatoes as peaches. If they bought 24 cans in all, how many of each did they buy?

2. Formulas start out being substitution problems. The formula for the volume of a cylinder is $V = \pi r^2 l$. What is the volume of a cylinder that is four inches in diameter and eighteen inches long? (Use $\frac{22}{7}$ for pi; r = radius, which is half the diameter, and l stands for length. Also, if there is no space between the variables, it means to multiply.)

3. Todd wanted to buy some trim for a window that was twice as high as it was wide. It took 24 feet of trim to go around the window. What were the lengths of all the sides?

4. If there were one more girl in Sue's Sunday School class, there would be twice as many girls as boys. If there were 14 children in her class, how many boys were there and how many girls?

SEQUENCE OF OPERATIONS FOR SUBSTITUTION

In a number sentence, some operations have preference over the others. Always perform the operations according to this plan.

1. **S**implify parentheses

2. **C**ompute powers and roots

3. **M**ultiply or divide

4. **A**dd or subtract

5. **D**ivide the denominator

Remember **SCMAD**

PRACTICE EXAMPLES

Solve these equations (Answers on page 248.)

1. $6 + 2 \cdot 4 =$ _____

2. $2 (3 + 5) (2 + 4) =$ _____

3. $3 + 4^3 =$ _____

4. $\dfrac{2 (5+3) (4-7)}{2 (9 - 11)} =$ _____

INVERSE OPERATIONS

Next to substitution, the most important tool in simplifying statements in algebra is the process called inverse operations.

As has been mentioned before, one of the goals in algebra is to get the variables on one side of the equals sign, and the numbers on the other.

In this equation, $X + 5 = 7$, the variable X is not alone. It's sharing its side of the equals sign with the **5**.

Logically, you can think, "What do I add to five to get 7?"

The other way to approach it is to subtract **5** from **both** sides of the equation. Hence, the name inverse. Since the sign in the equation calls for addition, it can be removed by subtraction. If the sign calls for subtraction, it can be removed by addition. The same is true for multiplication and division.

To refresh your memory, here is a list of the inverse processes.

THE INVERSE OF ADDITION IS SUBTRACTION

THE INVERSE OF SUBTRACTION IS ADDITION

THE INVERSE OF MULTIPLICATION IS DIVISION

THE INVERSE OF DIVISION IS MULTIPLICATION

PRACTICE EXAMPLES (Answers on page 248.)

Here are some examples that call for inverse operations to simplify.

1. $X - 9 = 14$

2. $3X = 21$

3. $2N + 6 = 16$

4. $4N - 3 = 3N$

PARENTHESES

We might do well to have a little practice with parentheses. Parentheses in a statement are like a package that says, "Open me first." A number or letter preceding the parentheses means multiply everything inside the parentheses by that number or letter. EVERYTHING!

Example: $8 (2 + 4) = (8 \times 2) + (8 \times 4) = 16 + 32 = 48$

Notice in this example that by adding the quantity inside the parentheses first, $8(6)$, you get 48. Do what's inside the parentheses first. Sometimes there are parentheses inside parentheses. Do the innermost first.

PRACTICE EXAMPLE

1. Bill saw a bargain table in the lumberyard. Everything on the table was priced at 89¢. He bought three screwdrivers, two files, and three clamps. How is this written in algebra? How much did Bill have to pay? (Answers on page 248.)

SIMULTANEOUS EQUATIONS

Here's an algebraic skill you might want to learn just because it looks so good. It's an excellent way to impress your friends.

A simultaneous equation occurs when you have more than one statement for the same set of variables.

Example:
$3W + Y = 19$ and $2W + Y = 14$

The problem is that it's tough enough to deal with one thing you don't know. It's harder still to think about two unknowns. You've got to get rid of one of them!

This can be done in the same way as always — inverse operations — and substitution — with some slight differences.

$3W + Y = 19$
$(2W + Y) = (14)$

Since the equation says that $2W + Y$ equals 14, you can add or subtract the unknowns on the "unknown" side and the numbers on the "number" side. This will fulfill the requirement of doing the same thing to both sides of the equation.

In this example, subtraction is the right operation to use, so — subtract!

$$\begin{array}{r} 3W + Y = 19 \\ - \ \underline{2W + Y = 14} \\ W + 0 = \ \ 5 \end{array}$$

This gets rid of the Y and lets you concentrate on W. By substituting 5 for W in the original equation you can now solve for Y.

$$\begin{array}{r} 3(5) + Y = 19 \\ 15 + Y = 19 \\ \text{Subtract} - 15 \quad \underline{-15} \\ Y = 4 \end{array}$$

Well, that's the procedure. Unfortunately, the real world isn't so accommodating. We picked an example that worked very easily. More often the equation will look something like this.

$$\begin{array}{r} 3Q + \ N = \ \ 16 \\ Q - 2N = -11 \end{array}$$

Not so tidy, right? The problem is still the same. You've got to do whatever's necessary to get rid of some of the unknowns. You must operate on the numbers and letters until one of the unknowns cancels itself out when you add or subtract.

In this case, you can get rid of the N by multiplying the top expression by 2. (Both sides, now!)

$$2 \times (3Q + N = 16) = \begin{array}{r} 6Q + 2N = \ \ 32 \\ \underline{Q - 2N = -11} \quad \text{Now add} \\ 7Q + 0 \ = \ \ 21 \end{array}$$

$$\dfrac{7Q}{7} = \dfrac{21}{7} \quad \text{Now divide}$$

$$Q = 3$$

(You could multiply the bottom equation by 3 and get rid of the Q):

$$\begin{array}{r} 3Q + \ \ N = \ \ 16 \\ \underline{-3Q - \ 6N = -33} \\ 7N = \ \ 49 \\ N = \ \ \ 7 \end{array}$$

It's a little tougher, but the result is the same.

PRACTICE EXAMPLES

Try these. (Answers on page 248.)

1. $2W - 2V = 8$

 $W + V = 8$

2. $Z + 2T = 14$

 $2Z - 2T = 10$

3. $4X + Y = 15$

 $X + \dfrac{Y}{2} = 5$

4. $4F - 3G = 0$

 $F + G = -7$

MONOMIALS AND POLYNOMIALS

It's a pity such basic parts of algebra have such threatening names.

A monomial (literally, one name) is an algebraic expression with just one term. A term is defined as a letter, or a number, or a group of numbers and letters, not separated by a plus or minus sign. Most of our work has been with monomials. For example, $2X$, $4ab$, $3N^2$, and $7abc$ are monomials.

A polynomial (which means many names) is an expression of more than one term. In a polynomial, the terms **ARE** separated by plus or minus signs. The operations with polynomials are similar to those with monomials. The only caution is THOSE TERMS WITH THE **SAME VARIABLES** MAY BE ADDED OR SUBTRACTED. (It's still the same thing — no oranges plus apples, please.)

$2X + 5Y$ is a polynomial.

Example of addition:

$$\begin{array}{r} 2X + 5Y \\ +3X + 2Y \\ \hline 5X + 7Y \end{array}$$

Example:

Simplify this statement.

$$3ab - 2a^2 + 3ab - 3a^2 + 6b + 4a^2 - b$$

To simplify an expression like this, put the same kinds of variables together the way the statement says to.

$$3ab - 2a^2 + 6b$$
$$+ \ 3ab - 3a^2 - \ \ b$$
$$\underline{\hspace{1.5cm} + \ 4a^2 \hspace{2.5cm}}$$
$$6ab - \ \ a^2 + 5b$$

This looks complex, but it is merely an application of all the things we've learned about the way numbers and unknowns go together.

PRACTICE EXAMPLES (Answers on page 248.)

1. $2m - 2n - 3m + 3n =$ _____

2. $(-7Q + W) + (Q - 2W) =$ _____

3. $m^2 + d^2 - 3m^2 + b^2 - 2d^2 =$ _____

4. $122 - 3f + 2a^2 + 22 + 2f - 4a^2 =$ _____

Polynomials can be (and are) multiplied and divided, too. Let's do that later.

MORE PRACTICE (Answers on page 248.)

Look in the student packet in the appendix for additional help.

Square Root - Use the averaging method to find the square root of the following numbers.

1. **A.** 841   _____

    B. 1296   _____

    C. 9604   _____

    D. 3481   _____

Find the values expressed by these powers.

2. **A.** 6^3 _____

    B. 3^6 _____

    C. 5^4 _____

    D. 10^9 _____

Pythagorean Theorem — Using the Pythagorean Theorem ($c^2 = a^2 + b^2$), find the following: (Answers on page 248.)

1.   Find c^2 if $a = 8$ and $b = 8$

2.   Find c if $a = 14$ and $b = 10$

3.   Find a^2 if $c^2 = 225$ and $b^2 = 81$

4.   In Problem 3, what is a?

VOCABULARY MATCHING (Answers on page 249.)

1. Root   **A.** $4\underline{x}$

2. Constant   **B.** $I = PRT$

3. Variable   **C.** 8^4

4. Literal Equation   **D.** $\underline{4}x$

5. Power   **E.** $\sqrt{}$

6. Simultaneous Equations   **F.** $8T + 2Y = 44$

                                  $T - Y = -2$

CUMULATIVE QUIZ (Answers on page 249.)

1. Solve these problems involving signed numbers.

   A. $(-7) - (-7) =$ _____

   B. $10 + (3 - 2 \cdot 4) =$ _____

   C. $-8 \cdot 4 + (2 - 6) =$ _____

   D. $-6 - 4 + 5 + 5 \cdot 2 =$ _____

2. Find the missing numbers.

   A. $\boxed{} + 3 = -7$

   B. $\boxed{} \cdot -3 = 9$

   C. $\dfrac{\boxed{}}{-7} = -15 + 8$

   D. $14 \div \boxed{} = -7$

3. Solve the following expressions.

   A. $2Y + 4 = 19$ $Y =$ _____

   B. $4 - Y = 15$ $Y =$ _____

   C. $2 + 7 \cdot 6 =$ _____

   D. $W^2 + 3 = 19$ $W =$ _____

4. In these literal equations, solve for the requested unknown.

   A. Find T in $C + T = W$ _____

   B. Find D in $W + 2D = Z$ _____

   C. Find Z in $Z^2 = N^2 + B^2$ _____

   D. Find A in $V = \dfrac{A}{D}$ _____

5. Find the square root of the following:

    A. $\sqrt{(484)}$ _____

    B. $\sqrt{(-3 + 4 \cdot 7)}$ _____

    C. $\sqrt{[4\,(-2 + 6)]}$ _____

    D. $\sqrt{B^2}$ _____

6. Three times what number is six more than 45?

7. If you can get three pots of geraniums and two pots of peonies for $5.30, and one pot of geraniums and two pots of peonies for $2.60, how much would two pots of geraniums cost?

8. Add seven apples, six pears, four oranges, two apples, three pears and two oranges.

My score on the Cumulative Quiz was _____ (number right).

EXTENDING YOUR UNDERSTANDING

In math and science, the need to express very large or very small numbers has led to a system often called "scientific notation."

We've talked about powers of numbers that tell how many times to multiply a number by itself. Scientific notation works on the powers of ten. 10^3 means $10 \times 10 \times 10$ or 1000.

Here's a way to work a problem using scientific notation: 4.63×10^3. Move the decimal point to the right as many places as the exponent says, 4.63 and fill in with zeroes, 4.630 = 4630.

Another example: $463 \times 10^3 = 463$ = 463,000

Try these: (Answers on page 250.)

1. **A.** 7.2×10^5

    B. 46×10^4

    C. 2.487×10^2

    D. 3.2×10^3

To express small numbers, scientific notation uses negative exponents.

   10^{-3} means .001

This can be accomplished by moving the decimal point to the **left** the number of places the exponent says.

Thus, 4.25×10^{-4} equals .000425. Got it?

PRACTICE EXAMPLES

2. **A.** 25×10^{-3}

    B. 25.3×10^{-4}

    C. $.05 \times 10^{-2}$

    D. 2×10^{-6}

CHAPTER THIRTEEN:

Shaping Up Your Geometry

1 PREVIEW

Geometry is perhaps the most poetic of the mathematical sciences. Its long history is filled with people who were looking for "truth." In this program, our friends look into these ancient understandings, and rediscover some of the principles that form the basis for geometry.

Geometry means to measure the earth. In the first scene, Todd and Bill do some measuring in an unlikely place, and discover that even on a tennis court, the laws of geometry still apply.

In the second scene, Bill and Frank investigate geometric figures. A great deal of what you need to know about geometry can be learned simply by using a compass and a straight edge to experiment with geometric figures.

Scene three gets into geometric proof. The students use simple formulas and their intuition to develop their own proofs for measure of area.

After you have viewed this program and done the assigned tasks in the workbook, you will have a better foundation for understanding geometry in the world around you.

Important Vocabulary

Acute — This refers to an angle that measures less than a right angle. It can be thought of as being **less** open than a right angle.

Altitude — In triangles other than right triangles, the height, or altitude, is not so easily seen sometimes. However, there is a procedure for finding the altitude of any triangle. It is important to know this, because many of the formulas for finding out other things about triangles require the use of the altitude.

Angle — The figure formed where two lines diverge from a common point.

Arc — A section of the circumference of a circle.

Area — Another way to measure a plane figure is by determining how much surface it contains. Area is measured in area units, or squares of a given size.

Base — Speaking of triangles, the base is the line from which the other lines and angles are measured. In a right triangle, it is either of the lines that form the right angle. You will hear two other terms that refer to the base of a triangle. They are height and altitude. In a right triangle these two terms are interchangeable. In a right triangle, the other line (not the base line) adjacent to the right angle is the height. A right triangle could be thought of as having lines that are base, height, and hypotenuse.

Circle — A curved closed line that is, at any point, the same distance from a point called the center.

Compass — This is one of the basic tools used in the study of geometry. In ancient times, the only tools a mathematician used were a compass and an unmarked straight edge (a ruler with no divisions marked on it.)

Congruent and Similar — These two terms are best thought of together. Congruent means the "same in every way." Two triangles are congruent if, when one is picked up and placed on the other, they exactly match. Similar means that they look alike, but are not the same size. In similar triangles, the angles are always the same. Only the lengths of the sides are different. Incidentally, **all** squares are similar.

Cube — A solid whose six faces are all congruent squares.

Degrees — The units in which angles are measured. A circle contains 360 degrees. The symbol (°) means "degrees."

Equilateral/Equiangular — This term is often used to describe a triangle that is very common. The words mean equal length of sides and equal size of angles. If a triangle is one of those things, it is both. Each angle of an equiangular triangle is sixty degrees. (Three angles of sixty add up to 180 degrees — the number allowed for a triangle.)

Euclid — He lived about 300 B.C. and was the great organizer of mathematical ideas. With very few exceptions, the rules he stated have been the basis for geometric thought since then. Often, the kind of geometry we are studying is called Euclidean Geometry.

Hypotenuse — In a right triangle, the side opposite the right angle is the longest of the three lines. It is called the hypotenuse.

Obtuse — Obtuse angles are greater than ninety degrees. They are **more** open than a right angle.

Parallel — Imagine a straight line in space, realizing that it can extend in both directions as far as you want it to. Now visualize another line beside it, drawn in such a way that it would always stay the same distance from the other. These lines are parallel. Railroad tracks are a practical example of parallel lines.

Perpendicular — Think of a horizontal line. Now imagine somewhere on it another line that is exactly ninety degrees on each angle. The second line is said to be perpendicular to the first.

Plane — Again, describing a plane and not sounding terribly mathematical is tough. Try this. If two points are connected, the result is the representation of a line. If more than two points are connected to make a closed figure, a plane is represented. Like the idea of a line, a plane does not really exist. It is an idea because it has length and width but no thickness. A triangle, square, hexagon and circle are planes. They have length and height but no depth.

Polygon — This is the general name given to plane figures. It means "many sides." Common polygons have special names, such as triangle, square, or hexagon. A figure of say, 17 sides, is usually called simply a polygon.

Protractor — In more modern times, the protractor was added to the tools used in geometry. It is a device to measure the size of angles. Protractors are divided into units of degrees and minutes and even seconds. (60 minutes to the degree, 60 seconds to the minute.)

Pythagoras — This is the name of a famous mathematician who lived 2,500 years ago. He is credited with having been the first person to record geometric rules.

Pythagorean Theorem — This is the most famous statement in geometry. You will hear it discussed many times and in different ways in this series. It states that $a^2 + b^2 = c^2$, where c is the length of the hypotenuse of a right triangle and a and b are the lengths of the other two sides.

Radius — The distance from the center of a circle to a point on the circle; it is equal to half the diameter of the circle.

Rectangle — Any four-sided geometric shape that has four right-angle corners.

Right Angle — As common as a right angle is, it is very difficult to explain in everyday terms. It is an angle of ninety degrees. If a circle is divided into four equal parts and lines are drawn through the center, the angles formed at the center are right angles. If you cut a pie very accurately into four pieces, the points of each piece are ninety degrees, or right angles. It makes sense that these would be ninety-degree angles since each piece is one fourth of a circle, and a circle, by definition, contains three hundred sixty degrees.

Right Triangle — A triangle that has one angle of ninety degrees is a right triangle. A triangle can have only one right angle. In a right triangle, the two angles that are **not right angles** must add up to ninety degrees. From this you can see that the sum of all the angles of a triangle is one hundred eighty degrees. This is true for all triangles, right or not.

Solid — If a figure has depth as well as length and height, it is called a solid. A cube, a pyramid, and a sphere are solid figures.

Square — A square is a specialized rectangle that has all right-angle corners and all four sides of the same length.

Vertex — In an angle, this is the "pointy" part.

GOAL SETTING EXERCISE (Answers on page 251.)

1. Answer the questions about the following angles. There may be more than one correct answer.

    A.   Which angle is a right angle?   _____

    B.   Which angle is an acute angle?   _____

    C.   Which angles are obtuse?   _____

    D.   Which angle is 180°?   _____

    E.   Which angle is more than 180°?   _____

    F.   Which angle is the smallest?   _____

    G.   Which angle is perpendicular to the base?   _____

U   V   W   X   Y

2. Answer these questions about the following figures.

    A.   Which triangle includes a right angle?   _____

    B.   Which triangle is equiangular?   _____

    C.   Which triangle is equilateral?   _____

    D.   Which figure (or figures) is/are rectangles?   _____

    E.   Which figure (or figures) is/are polygons?   _____

    F.   Which figures include obtuse angles?   _____

    G.   Which figures include acute angles?   _____

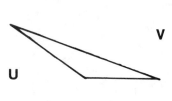 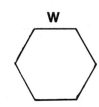 

3. Find the perimeter of the following figures.

A. Triangle   _____

B. Square   _____

C. Rectangle   _____

D. Hexagon   _____

E. Circle (Circumference)   _____

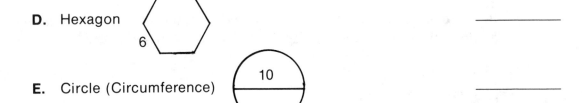

4. Find the area of the following figures. The formula for each is given. Remember, the answer is stated in the number of squares it would take to cover the entire surface.

   A. Area of a rectangle = length times width.

   B. Area of a square = side times side (length times width).

   C. Area of a triangle = $\frac{1}{2}$ base times the height.

   D. Area of a circle = pi times the radius squared (times itself).

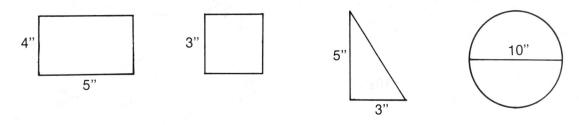

5. What is the volume of a cube that is six inches on a side?

6. In the following illustration, if the circle has a radius of five feet, what is the length of line X?

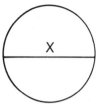

7. Sue wants to buy enough tile that are a foot square to cover the floor of a room that is nine feet by nine feet. How many will it take?

8. Todd wants to paint the sides of an octagonal (8-sided) gazebo. Each side is six feet wide and eight feet high. Ignoring any openings, how many square feet of surface must he paint?

9. If you were going to cut a pie into four equal pieces, what is the degree of the angle at the point of each piece? In five pieces? In six pieces?

2 GOAL PROFILE

Put a check in the box that fits your situation.

When You Watch the Program

☐ A. If you got all of them right, ... Euclid, stand back! We've got a new genius on our hands. Still, pay close attention to Bill when he develops the formula for the area of a hexagon.

☐ B. If you missed any part of number 1, then .... Study the page in the appendix that tells about angles. Listen carefully to the tennis court scene.

☐ C. If you missed any part of number 2, then .... Review what you know about triangles and listen to the discussion of the Pythagorean Theorem.

☐ D. If you missed any part of number 3, then .... Pay particular attention to Bill's explanation of what the hexagon is telling him.

☐ E. If you missed any part of
       number 4, then . . . .   Review the part of the appendix that
                                                         talks about area and perimeter. Be
                                                         especially alert to the third scene.

☐ F. If you missed any part of
       number 5, then . . . .   This is a solid figure. Study the page
                                                         in the appendix that talks about volume,
                                                         and be sure to listen to the parts of the
                                                         next two programs dealing with volume.

☐ G. If you missed any part of
       number 6, then . . . .   Circles figure in the next three
                                                         programs. Be awake!

☐ H. If you missed any part of
       number 7, then . . . .   Area is discussed several times from
                                                         here on in the series. Be sure you listen
                                                         to Steve Wise.

☐ I.   If you missed any part of
       number 8, then . . . .   This is a "surface of a solid" problem. It
                                                         is a multiplication of several areas. There
                                                         will be more on this in the study section
                                                         of this chapter.

☐ J. If you missed any part of
       number 9, then . . . .   Remember, a circle contains 360°. When
                                                         it is divided into a specific number of
                                                         even pieces, the angle of each division
                                                         is that fractional part of the 360°.

3 NOW YOU ARE READY TO WATCH THE PROGRAM, "SHAPING UP YOUR GEOMETRY."

4 REACT, PRACTICE, AND EXTEND. (Answers on page 251.)

1. Here are some facts about angles. By using this information answer the questions.

A.

< CAB = 20°

< DAB = 42°

What is < DAC? _____

B.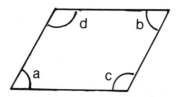

< a = 45°   < b = 45°

What are angles c & d? _____

2. Here are some triangles. Find the area of each one. (A = $\frac{1}{2}$ bh)*

A. 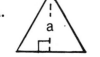 b = 9

a = 12

*(For some reason, you find the "altitude" but when you compute, it's called "height.")

B. 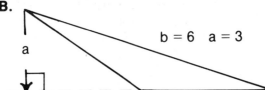 b = 6   a = 3

3. Find the length of the line indicated by each letter.

A.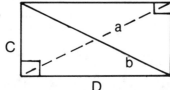

C = 6   b = 10.8

D = 9   a = _____

B.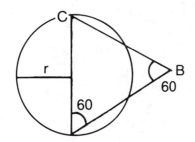

r = 10

Find CB _____

4. Use the Pythagorean Theorem to find the length of the indicated side of each right triangle.

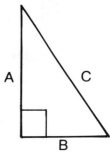

A. A = 7   B = 4   C = _____

B. A = 9   B = 9   C = _____

C. B = 4   C = 11   A = _____

D. C = 14.14   A = 10   B = _____

SIMILAR TRIANGLES

One reason for the invention of geometry, according to legend, is that once in the Nile Valley, a period of flood erased all land markings. After the water receded and the farmers returned to their land, they needed some system to compute property lines from landmarks that would not be destroyed.

One of the many ways this was done is called "triangulation." It has to do with the fact that in similar triangles the angles are the same and the sides are proportionate. Remember our old friend proportion?

Look at this drawing. It is like the one that Todd described on the tennis court.

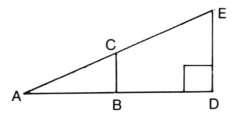

If we draw that illustration a little differently, it becomes a more useful tool for finding how far things are from each other. You will often see this illustration in books about geometry.

Fig. 1

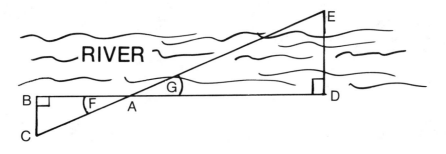

Here's the way it works.

Suppose you need to know how far it is from point D to point E, but there is a raging river in between. However, if you stand at point A and sight a straight line, and have a friend mark points B and D with line AB being half as long as line AD, you'll find out that line BC is half as long as line DE. (Actually, you could make the triangle that's on dry land the same size as the one that crosses the river, but then where would be the mathematical challenge?)

For example, if the distance from B to A is twenty yards and the distance from A to D is forty yards, **AND** the distance from B to C is fifteen yards, then the distance across

the river would be thirty yards. $\dfrac{20}{15} = \dfrac{40}{X}$ Got it?

The triangles don't have to be connected like the one in the drawing, but because of the interior angle rule (Appendix), this makes it easier to be sure the triangles are similar. Suppose you wanted to measure the height of a tree in your yard. It's too tall to climb, but you can measure its shadow. The shadows cast by vertical objects form similar triangles so the same rules apply. Study this illustration and determine how high the tree is. (Answers on page 252.)

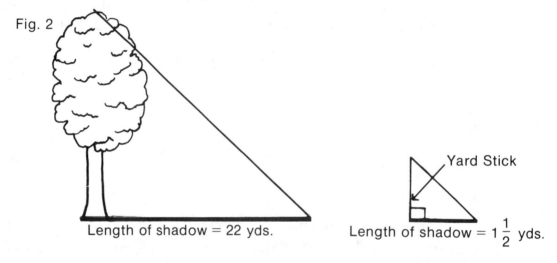

Fig. 2

Length of shadow = 22 yds.

Yard Stick

Length of shadow = $1\frac{1}{2}$ yds.

In the illustration in Figure 1, what is the distance from A to E? (Clue: This time it would be easier to use the Pythagorean Theorem, but in real life you could double the distance from C to A.)

VOCABULARY MATCHING (Answers on page 252.)

1. Right angle

2. Hypotenuse

3. Plane

4. Vertex

5. Equilateral

6. Perimeter

A. The side in a right triangle opposite the right angle.

B. An imaginary surface in space that has length and width but no depth.

C. An angle that measures 90°.

D. The distance around a figure.

E. A figure that has all sides the same length.

F. The point where an angle is formed.

CUMULATIVE QUIZ (Answers on page 252.)

1. See how you can do on these signed number exercises.

    A. $-7 (3 + 2) + (8 - 12) = $ _____

    B. $-2 - (3 \cdot 4) + (3 \cdot 2) = $ _____

    C. $3 (2 - 8) (3 - 6) = $ _____

    D. $4 + (3 \cdot 2)^2 - 7 = $ _____

2. See how you can do on these problems that have to do with inverse operations.

    A. $2W + 4 = 10$

    B. $2X^2 = 32$

    C. $2Y + 4 = 3Y + 6$

    D. $4 - Q = 2 + 2Q$

3. Solve these power problems.

    A. 8^2

    B. 3^4

   C. 2^8

   D. 7^3

4. Compute the square roots of these numbers.

   A. 729

   B. 2809

   C. 169

   D. 7744

5. Solve for the requested unknown.

   A. In CW = Z, solve for W

   B. In C = π D, solve for D

   C. In I = PRT, solve for R

   D. In V = π r²1, solve for 1

6. Find the area of these figures.

A.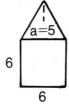

B.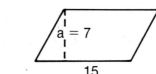

7. Todd is six feet tall. He noticed his shadow was exactly eight feet long. His son is four feet tall. How long is his son's shadow?

8. Sue noticed the windows in her kitchen are perfect squares that are three feet high. If there are four such windows, how many square feet of glass do they contain?

EXTENDING YOUR UNDERSTANDING

The exact value of pi has fascinated mathematicians for centuries. Sometimes, we've used 22/7 as its value, but 3.1416 is a little more accurate. Pi is an irrational number. That is, it never comes out even, and no matter how many places it is carried out, the numbers never repeat themselves in sequence. With the help of computers, people have carried out the value more than 10,000 places beyond the decimal point.

Even the crude value, 22/7, is only .04% worse than the most often used estimate and it is generally assumed that there is no "exact" value for pi.

One of the perplexing problems of Euclidean geometry has been called "squaring a circle." It is another will-o-the-wisp. The idea is to use only a compass and an unmarked straight edge to construct a square equal in area to a given circle. You might try it. It can be addictive, though, so be careful.

CHAPTER FOURTEEN:

How Many? How Long? How Big? How Full? How Heavy?

1 PREVIEW

Many times every day we measure things. Maybe we don't actually get out the yardstick or a scale, but we are continually evaluating quantity in our minds.

Such questions as, "Do I have time to mow the lawn before dinner?", "Will the closet hold all these clothes?", "Is this the coldest (hottest) day of the year?", or "I wonder how much material it takes to make this skirt?" All these common wonderments are measurements or questions of quantity.

This is the way measurement occurs most often. For the most part, we are looking for a quick estimate, a simple relationship, or a "ballpark figure."

Sometimes more precision is required. If you are going to buy drapery material, you need to have a fairly close idea of how much you need. Because of the expense involved, you don't want to purchase far too much, but you certainly don't want to get four inches too little.

In this program, you will get several glimpses of people using measures of different kinds. Because measure is such a continual activity, we have come up with ways to measure practically everything. When you measure, you are always confronted with the need to convert, or interchange, one measure for another.

Frank makes a very important point in the first scene. Because there are so many things to measure, it's impossible to remember all the conversion ratios. One skill everyone needs to develop is accuracy in reading conversion tables.

In scene two, you'll learn that in practical use, the first measurement usually isn't enough. Knowing the area of a wall to be covered with bricks isn't particularly useful. What you really want to know is how many bricks you'll need and what they will cost. In most cases, the information you are seeking takes more than one step to find.

If you think creatively about scene three, you'll understand why many poor farmers in the days of the Great Depression built their chicken runs in the shape of a circle.

Important Vocabulary

Conversion — In this series, this term refers to expressing measures in different units. For instance, conversion of one foot to inches and so forth. Some texts use the term "interchanging" to mean the same thing.

Cubic Measure — Volume is measured by counting the number of cubes of a certain size necessary to completely fill a solid.

English System — The names for measures most commonly used in the United States were borrowed from England, hence the name. **Feet, quarts, yards, miles,** and **acres** are all English System units.

Length and Girth — This is a term used in a post office to determine the size of a package being mailed. Length is, as you would suspect, the length of the longest side. Girth, in this case, is the perimeter of the smallest dimension.

Linear Measure — Linear means "like a line." All distance measures are linear, even if the line isn't straight. A line is thought to have no width or thickness; only length.

Metric System — Most of the world operates on the metric system of measures. This is a far more scientific approach to measuring. It is a decimal system and therefore easier to convert to other units. Kilometer, centimeter, liter, meter, and hectare are all metric units.

Proportion — This term is especially important in this program. Proportion is a method of comparing more than one ratio.

Ratio — You'll remember this term from earlier programs. Ratio is a way of comparing two numbers by division.

Simplify — As this term is used in this lesson, it means to find the simplest units of measure in which an answer can be expressed. For example, five thousand, two hundred, ninety feet is expressed more simply as one mile and ten feet.

Solids and Planes — You will remember these terms from the geometry program. Check Chapter Three for more precise definitions. For this program, think of a plane as a flat surface that has no thickness. If what you see does have thickness, it's a solid. (Solids have three dimensions . . . height, width, and depth . . . or words that mean the same thing like "thickness," "tall," "wide," "deep," "across," etc.)

Square Measure — If a measure has length **and** width and you want to determine the size of the surface, the answer is expressed in the number of squares of a certain size it would take to cover the surface. In measure of area, you count the number of squares in a figure.

2 GOAL SETTING EXERCISE

Solve these sets of exercises. (Answers on page 253.)

  1. Convert the following measures.

   A. 6 gallons = _____ quarts

   B. 84 inches = _____ feet

   C. 9 hours = _____ minutes

   D. 12 pounds = _____ ounces

2. Convert the following measures to yards.

    A. 72 inches = _____ yards

    B. 2 miles = _____ yards

    C. 7 feet = _____ yards

3. Fill in the missing words.

    A. 6 _____ = $1\frac{1}{2}$ quarts

    B. 3 _____ = 9 feet

    C. 4000 _____ = 2 tons

4. Area is measured in squares of a certain size. Find the area of the figures below and express them in the terms requested.

    A. [square] = _____ sq. yds.
    2 yds. / 2 yds.

    B. [rectangle] = _____ sq. ft.
    6 in. / 48 in.

    C. [rectangle] = _____ sq. in.
    2 ft. / 3 ft.

    D. [rectangle] = _____ sq. yd.
    6 ft. / 7 ft.

5. Add the following measure problems and express them in the requested form.

    A.   5 ft. 7 in.
       +4 ft. 11 in.   = _____ yds. _____ ft. _____ in.

    B.   2 qts. 1 pt.
       3 qts.
       4 qts. 1 pt.
      +2 qts. 3 pt.   = _____ gal. _____ qts. _____ pts.

C. 2 da. 5 hr.
  4 da. 7 hr.
  +3 da. 14 hr.   = _____ wks. _____ da. _____ hr.

D. 7 yrs. 4 mo.
  8 yrs. 2 mo.
  +9 yrs. 10 mo.   = _____ decades _____ yrs. _____ mo.

6. Subtract the following examples.

A. 3 gal. 3 qt.
  −1 gal. 2 qt.

B. 6 hrs. 27 min.
  −2 hrs. 14 min.

C. 15 yds. 1 ft.
  − 1 yd. 2 ft.

D. 2 tons 963 pounds
  −   1670 pounds

7. Sue had a square yard of material. She wanted to cut it into quilt patches nine inches by nine inches. How many squares did she get?

8. Todd's electric bill tells his monthly usage in kilowatt hours. In April he used 756 kilowatt hours, in May 689, and in June 654. If he pays 5¢ per kilowatt hour, how much is his total bill for the three months?

9. Martha bought 14 quarts of strawberries, which she wants to share evenly with Sue, Todd, and Bill. How much will each of them get? (Express your answer in terms of quarts and pints.)

10. How many cubic inches are in a cubic foot?

GOAL PROFILE

Put a check in the box that fits your situation.

When You Watch the Program

☐ A. If you got all of them
  right, ...   You certainly do measure up! Still, you may want to study the conversion charts in the study section of the chapter.

☐ B. If you missed any part of number 1 or 2, ... Be sure you understand the proportion system Frank tells the class about.

☐ C. If you missed any part of number 3, then .... These are common measures. You need to memorize the conversion ratios for these.

☐ D. If you missed any part of number 4, then .... Pay particular attention to scene two.

☐ E. If you missed any part of number 5 or 6, ... Martha and Sue work with addition and subtraction of measures. Be sure you understand what they say.

☐ F. If you missed any part of number 7, then .... This is a problem involving surface. Scene three will help you.

☐ G. If you missed any part of number 8, then .... This is more of a simple addition and multiplication problem than it is an exercise in measure. It is much like what happens in scene two.

☐ H. If you missed any part of number 9, then .... Pay close attention to scene two.

☐ I. If you missed any part of number 10, then .... Be especially alert to scene three. Review the section on powers and roots in Chapter Three.

3 NOW YOU ARE READY TO WATCH THE PROGRAM, "HOW MANY? HOW LONG? HOW BIG? HOW FULL? HOW HEAVY?"

4 REACT, PRACTICE, AND EXTEND. (Answers on page 253.)

1. Here are some examples like the ones in the program. Use the proportion system to convert these measures.

    A. How many feet in three miles?

    B. How many gallons in 82 quarts?

    C. How many ounces in 13 pounds?

    D. How many minutes in 7 hours?

2. Bill bought 300 feet of rope. He sold Todd 16 yards. How much did he have left?

3. Solve these addition examples.

    A.   3 lbs. 12 oz.   B.   12 hrs. 20 min. 36 sec.
         2 lbs. 9 oz.   11 hrs. 48 min. 22 sec.
        +7 lbs. 14 oz.   +17 hrs. 29 min. 52 sec.

    C.   3 wks. 4 days 2 hrs.   D.   2 decades 8 yrs. 4 mo.
        +2 wks. 4 days 14 hrs.   +3 decades 9 yrs. 10 mo.

4. Solve these subtraction examples. (You will need to regroup.)

    A.   2 hrs. 7 min.   B.   5 tons   980 lbs.
        −1 hr. 22 min.   −1 ton   1632 lbs.

    C.   2 cubic yds.   D.   16 yrs. 4 mos.
        −   6 cu. ft.   − 1 yr. 10 mos.

Multiplication requires a slightly different approach. You must remember to multiply each unit by the multiplier. Then the parts must be converted and put together.

Example: 7 ft. 3 in.
            $\times$ 7
            ─────────────
            49 ft. 21 in.   Convert to 1 ft. 9 inches and add

            49 ft.
             1 ft. 9 in.
            ─────────────
            50 ft. 9 in.

5. Try these now.

A.   4 gal. 2 qts.   **B.**   2 yds. 1 ft.
    $\times$ 8 $\times$ 6

C.   5 lbs. 12 oz.   **D.**   3 hrs. 16 min.
    $\times$ 9 $\times$ 14

Division is similar to multiplication. Be sure to keep the units separated.

Example: 4 ft. 10 in.
                 ──────────────
              3) 14 ft.   6 in.
                 12
                 ──
(Convert 2 ft.   2 $\times$ 12 = 24   Add 6 in. and 24 in.
to 24 in.)   30   Then divide again.
                                 ──
                                 30

6. Try these.

A.   **B.**
     ─────────────   ─────────────
    2) 3 gal.   2 qts.   4) 6 yds. 2 ft.

C. ─────────────   **D.** ─────────────
    3) 51 lbs. 4 oz.   7) 3 qts.   1 pt.

CONVERSION CHARTS

Being familiar with conversion charts is an important part of dealing with measures. As Frank says, there's no need to remember the conversion rate of anything other than the most common of measures. You can look up others when you need them.

Conversion charts for measures generally come in two types. The one below is an **Equivalents Table**.

1 qt. = 2 pt.

1 gal. = 4 qt.

1 ft. = 12 in.

1 yd. = 3 ft.

1 mi. = 5280 ft.

1 mi. = 1760 yd. *(See Below)

The advantage of this type of chart is that you are set up to do the proportion system talked about in the TV program.

Example: How many yards are in 7 miles?

$$* \quad \frac{1 \text{ mi.}}{1760 \text{ yd.}} = \frac{7 \text{ mi.}}{X} = X = 12{,}320$$

Seven miles = 12,320 yards.

Another common conversion table is a **Multiplier Chart.** It is used by many engineers and scientists. Here is a sample **Multiplier Chart**.

MULTIPLY	BY	TO OBTAIN
Acres	43,560	Sq. Ft.
Fathoms	6	Feet
Feet	12	Inches
Gallons	8	Pts. (Liq.)
Gallons	4	Qts. (Liq.)
Ounces	.0625	Pounds
Miles	1.609×10^5	Centimeters

This type of chart has two advantages: It can be alphabetized so units are easy to find, and **it works well both ways.** (Inverse operations, you know.)

Acres times 43,560 equals square feet **and** square feet **divided** by 43,560 equals acres. Since the multipliers are generally listed in decimal form, answers come out in fractional parts.

Conversion multipliers of very large, or very small, numbers are expressed in **scientific notation.** (See page 162 in this workbook.)

Example: Miles $\times$ 1.069 $\times$ 10^5 = Centimeters

A. How many centimeters are in 3 miles?

3 $\times$ 1.069 $\times$ 10^5 = 3·106900 = 320,700 Centimeters in 3 mi.

B. How many miles in a million centimeters?

1,000,000 $\div$ 1.069 $\times$ 10^5 = 1,000,000 $\div$ 106900 = 9.35 mi.

1. Try these. (Answers on page 255.)

Multiply	By	To Obtain
Sq. In.	6.944 $\times$ 10^{-3}	Sq. Ft.
Watts	1.341 $\times$ 10^{-3}	Horsepower

A. How many square feet are in a million square inches?

B. How much horsepower is a kilowatt (1000 watts)?

C. How many watts in one horsepower?

VOCABULARY MATCHING (Answers on page 255.)

The terms on the right have something to do with the terms on the left. Can you match them up?

1. Metric System		**A.** Volume
2. English System		**B.** Triangle
3. Cubic measure		**C.** Pint
4. Plane		**D.** Ratio
5. Proportion		**E.** Liter

CUMULATIVE QUIZ (Answers on page 255.)

1. Solve these equations involving signed numbers.

    A. $(+9) + (-15) =$ _____

    B. $(-7) + (+4) + (+6) + (-2) =$ _____

    C. $(+4) - (-4) =$ _____

    D. $(-12) - (-8) - (+6) =$ _____

2. Solve these problems of multiplication and division.

    A. $(-23) \cdot (-3) =$ _____

    B. $(-7) \cdot (+4) =$ _____

    C. $(-6) \div (-2) =$ _____

    D. $(-36) \div (+4) =$ _____

3. Solve the following expressions.

    A. $2Q + 7 = 25 - 6$ $Q =$ _____

    B. $3ab + 6 = 20 - 2$ $ab =$ _____

    C. $B^2 - 60 = \sqrt{16}$ $B =$ _____

    D. $X + 6 = 2$ $X =$ _____

4. Solve these literal equations for each requested unknown.

    A. Find Z in $C + Z = Q$

    B. Find P in $\frac{G}{P} = S$

    C. Find B in $A = \frac{B}{2} \cdot H$

    D. Find W in $X + \sqrt{W} = T$

5. Find the area of the following figures.

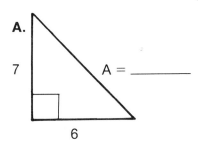

A. A = _____

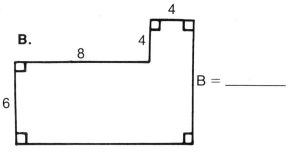

B. B = _____

6.   How much would it cost to carpet a 9' x 12' room if carpet costs $16 a square yard?

7.   At $1.20 a quart, how much does six gallons of motor oil cost?

8.   Sue wants to buy some lace at 38¢ a foot. How much will four yards cost?

9.   Bill needs seven boards four feet seven inches long. How much waste will he have if he cuts them out of four boards ten feet long? (Ignore the sawdust.)

10.   If the boards in Problem 9 cost $1.20 per linear foot, and you lose $\frac{1}{8}$ of an inch each cut, what is the total value of the sawdust?

Cumulative quiz score _____ (number right)

EXTENDING YOUR UNDERSTANDING (Answers on page 256.)

In measuring something, the "yardstick" you select must be appropriate to the measuring you intend to do. It would be foolish to measure a mile with a measuring stick an inch long. First, it would take you forever to do it, and it would be terribly inaccurate. Being human, each time you put down your inch-long measuring stick, you would make a slight error. This error accumulates. Since there are 63,360 inches in a mile, you'd make **that many errors.**

As a rule of thumb, it is best to use the measure closest to the size of what you want to measure. This is why astronomers use a very large "yardstick" when they measure the vast distances of space. A common measure for interstellar space is the **light year.** A light year is the distance that light travels in a year's time. Light travels very fast, **186,000 miles per second.** The nearest star (other than the sun) is four and one-half light years away. That is something over **26 trillion** miles. Obviously, the mile is not good for measuring space.

To practice selecting a good measuring device, solve the following problems in your head. Just choose the most appropriate measure for the job. (You can have some fun with your friends with this.)

Choose among these to measure . . .

Inches	Ounces
Feet	Pounds
Yards	Tons
Miles	Ounces (liquid)
Light years	Pints
Barrels	Quarts
	Gallons

. . . these . . .

A. The length of a million one-dollar bills laid end to end.

B. The distance a snail can travel in a day.

C. The snow is a foot deep on an acre of ground. You stack it all up in a pile that is a foot square.

D. A frog's tongue.

E. With a teaspoon you start to make a pile of sand. The first day you move one teaspoon, the next day two teaspoons, the next day four, and so on, doubling the number of spoons you move every day for three weeks.

F. The weight of an average-sized, white, fluffy cloud.

G. A newborn kangaroo.

H. The honey produced by one good hive of bees in a month.

I. The weight of the air on a card table.

J. A pound of gold.

K. The blood in your body.

L. The amount of maple sap to make a teaspoon of maple syrup.

M. Vanilla extract in a ton of homemade ice cream.

N. Milk from a goat in a day.

STEVE WISE SAYS

When using the proportion system for conversion, be certain to set up the fractions so the units appear in the same place.

FEET   **FEET**   **FEET**
Inches   =   Inches   =   Inches

When adding or subtracting measures, be sure to keep the same kinds of units lined up in columns.

Feet	Inches
4 ft.	3 in.
2 ft.	6 in.
9 ft.	1 in.
15 ft.	10 in.

The shape of a figure changes the relationship of the perimeter to the area.

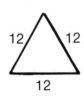

$$P = 36 \qquad\qquad P = 36$$

$$A = 62.29 \qquad\quad A = 81$$

Don't forget to work on Todd's fish problem.

Head   =   9"

Body   =   Head + $\frac{1}{2}$ Tail

Tail   = $\frac{1}{2}$ Head + Body

CHAPTER FIFTEEN:

"The James"

1 **PREVIEW**

In order to solve most math problems, it is necessary to "get inside" the workings and see what's there.

That's what this program is all about.

In scene one, Frank gives the students a plan for gaining access to the solution of tough problems.

Scene two shows how this technique can be used to work pretty complex mathematics.

This brings us to scene three. In this scene, we finally get the solution to Todd's fish problem.

After you have seen this program and completed the exercises in the workbook, you should be able to approach most everyday algebra and geometry problems with confidence and a more positive outlook.

Important Vocabulary

No new terms are used in this program.

2 **GOAL SETTING EXERCISE** (Answers on page 258.)

1. Solve the following problems with the information supplied.

Apples always cost half as much as oranges.

Pears always cost 18¢.

Lemons always cost as much as one apple plus one pear.

A. If lemons cost 34¢ each, how much are oranges?

B. If apples cost 28¢, how much are lemons?

C. If oranges cost 30¢, how much are lemons?

D. If apples are 28¢ each, how much are six oranges and six lemons?

2. Sue is a year and a half younger than her sister. Her brother is now half the age of their mother. Their father is two years older than their mother.

   A. If their father is 58, how old is Sue's brother?

   B. If their mother was 24 when Sue was born, how old was she when Sue's sister was born?

   C. If Sue's brother is three years older than her sister, what can you say about Sue's age in regard to the age of her brother?

   D. When her father is 64, he will be twice as old as Sue. How old will Sue's sister be then?

3. The perimeter of a triangle is 66 inches. The first side is 8 inches less than the second. The third is two inches less than the first. What is the length of each side?

4. Bill can build a dog house in four days. It would take Todd six days to build the same dog house. How long would it take them working together?

5. Find the volume of the figures below.

A.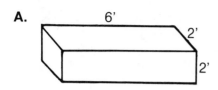

B.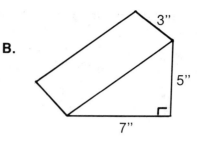

C.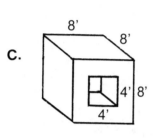

D.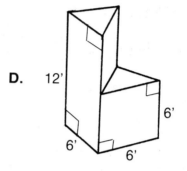

*Clue: Deduct the volume of the hole.

6. Martha planted a rectangular flower bed. The short
sides were half as long as the long sides. The area
was eight square yards. What was the perimeter?

7. If you had three containers . . . one holds eight pints,
one holds five pints, and a third holds two pints . . .
how could you measure just one pint?

8. If there are 640 acres in a square mile, how many
square feet are in an acre?

9. Bill installed a light over the stairs to his basement.
He leaves it burning all the time. If he put a 40 watt
bulb in it, and he pays five cents per kilowatt hour,
how long can the light remain on before it costs him a
dollar? (A kilowatt is 1000 watts.)

10. A bookworm is eating its way through a set of encyclopedia. Each volume is two and one-half inches thick, including the covers, which are one-eighth inches thick each. Including the pages and covers, how far must the worm travel from the last page of volume one to page 1 of volume two?

GOAL PROFILE

Put a check in the box that fits your situation.

When You Watch the Program

☐ A. If you got all of them
       right, ...

Very impressive! Still you might want to browse through the appendix of this workbook before you watch the program.

☐ B. If you missed any part of
       number 1, then ....

You need the "James". Follow Steve Wise's comments after the first scene.

☐ C. If you missed any part of
       number 2, then ....

The first scene is important to you. It will tell you how to get inside problems like this.

☐ D. If you missed any part of
       number 3, then ....

It might be a good idea for you to review the chapter on geometry before you watch the program.

☐ E. If you missed any part of
       number 4, then ....

Scene one will help you. You might want to review the chapter on algebra before you try the TV program.

☐ F. If you missed any part of
       number 5, then ....

Review the geometry chapter and pay particular attention to scene two.

☐ G. If you missed any part of
       number 6, then ....   Review both the algebra chapter and the
                                         geometry chapter before you watch this
                                         program.

☐ H. If you missed any part of
       number 7, then ....   This one works better with common
                                         sense than it does with math. What
                                         does Steve Wise say about that?

☐ I. If you missed any part of
       number 8, then ....   Try to draw a picture of this situation
                                         before you view the program.

☐ J. If you missed any part of
       number 9, then ....   Review the chapter on measure before
                                         you watch the program.

☐ K. If you missed any part of
       number 10, then ....   Can you draw a picture of this one? What
                                         does Steve Wise have to say about
                                         common sense?

3 NOW YOU ARE READY TO WATCH THE PROGRAM, "THE JAMES."

You have surely noticed that the goal-setting questions were different in this chapter. As you watch, try to analyze the scenes and see how many applications of the material can be made. If you had more difficulty with the Goal Setting Exercise than usual, there will be some additional help for you later.

4 REACT, PRACTICE, AND EXTEND. (Answers on page 259.)

Before we go on, let's investigate the "james" a little more.

Step 1 of the "james."

DRAW A PICTURE OF WHAT THE PROBLEM IS ALL ABOUT.

If you can do this, you have clearly in your mind what is happening in the problem. The reason for this step is to visualize, or find the **quality**, of the relationships.

Let's practice drawing some pictures.

1. Take a coin and draw a circle around it. Now with the same coin, draw as many circles as you can around the circumference of the first one so they are just touching, but not overlapping.

When you've completed the drawing, consider these questions.

A. How many circles **just fit** around the circumference?

B. How does the size of the circle affect these relationships?

C. How can this information be used?

Another one:

Draw a horizontal line on a scrap of paper. At the left end of that line, draw another line toward the top of your paper at a right angle to the first. Make this second line twice the length of the first. (Just guess.)
From this ending point, draw a diagonal line to form a triangle.

A. Do you have a right triangle with the base half as long as the altitude?

B. Is the smallest angle near the top of your page?

C. Now here's the hard question. Can you tell the length of all the lines in relation to the first line you drew?

Step two of the "james."

ASSIGN VARIABLES

Look again at the pictures you just drew.
The first one is governed entirely by geometric laws. It makes no difference whether you draw around a dime or a garbage can lid, six circles just exactly fit around one.
If you call the first circle "C," then the number you can draw around it is 6C.

The second drawing is governed by geometry, too.

If you call the first line you drew "X," the base, then the second line is 2X because it's twice as long. Once these two dimensions are established, the length of the third line, the hypotenuse, is set. You can't make it any longer or shorter or it won't meet the ends of the first two lines.

Now, remembering the Pythagorean Theorem, you know if a square is constructed on side X and a square is constructed on side 2X, then a square constructed on the hypotenuse is the sum of these first two squares. The square of X is X^2, and the square of 2X is $(2X)^2$.

Be careful with this last one — it is not the same quantity as $2X^2$. For instance, if X is 3, $(2X)^2$ is 6^2 or 36, while $2X^2$ is 2 times 9 or 18. $(2X)^2$ actually equals $4X^2$ (you square everything inside the parentheses).

And, to find the length of the hypotenuse, you must find the square root of the sum of the other two squares.

With this information, the hypotenuse in this picture can be labeled $\sqrt{X^2 + (2X)^2}$.

This brings us to the Step Three of the "james."

WORK IT WITH EASY NUMBERS FIRST

In the triangle you drew, you have a picture of **every** right triangle in the world that has the sides X and 2X.

Check it out now with easy numbers. Substitute any number you want for X, preferably a small one, and solve for the other two sides. Now you're set up to answer practically any question about that triangle. You can find the area ($A = \frac{1}{2} X \cdot 2X$). You can tell about the perimenter ($P = X + 2X + \sqrt{X^2 + (2X)^2}$. You get the idea.

Once you're convinced you understand your drawing, substitute numbers in the problems you're trying to solve and find the unknown.

It is likely you can solve any problem you can draw a picture of.

TRANSLATING ENGLISH TO ALGEBRA

Look at these translations from the TV program, along with the examples of how they are frequently used.

1.   Six less than something.   X – 6

Bill's pay check was six dollars less than usual. If his check was $220, what is it normally?

2.   Something less than six.   6 – X

Martha was expecting six guests, but only three had arrived. How many weren't there yet?

4. Five more than something.   X + 5

Sue canned five more quarts of beans on Wednesday than she did on Tuesday. She canned fifteen quarts on Wednesday. How many did she do on Tuesday?

5. Five more than twice something.   2X + 5

Todd had a good week at the paint store. He sold twice as much paint as he ever had before. Then, at closing time, he sold five additional gallons. When he totaled the sales for this record week, he found he had sold 185 gallons. What was his previous record?

6. Some number increased by twenty.   X + 20

Martha's club made twenty toy alligators one afternoon. Added to what they already had, they had enough to mail 75 alligators. How many did they have to start with?

7. Twenty increased by some number.   20 + X

Bill thought he had $20, but to his surprise, he found a check stuck away in his billfold. Now he knew he had $45. How big was the check?

8. Some number decreased by nine.   X − 9

Albany is nine miles closer than Montpelier. If Montpelier is 35 miles away, how far is Albany?

9. Sue's age fourteen years from now.   X + 14

Sue said, "In 14 years, I'll be a half century old. How old is she now?

10. Bill's age ten years ago.   X − 10

Ten years ago, Bill was 26. How old is he now?

There are many other translations, but these occur often in everyday experiences. Be alert, though, because these translations frequently appear in combination. For instance, five times what number is five less than six times ten?

In algebra this would be 5N = 6(10) − 5   N = 11.

FORMULAS (Answers on page 259.)

Most people use algebra to solve problems for which there is already a plan for finding the solution.

Below are some formulas and some story problems. You'll need to select the formula that gives you the desired answer and substitute the values listed in the problem.

Area of square	$A = s^2$
Area of a rectangle	$A = lw$
Area of a circle	$A = \pi r^2$
Circumference of a circle	$C = \pi d$
Volume of a rectangular solid	$V = lhw$
Volume of a cube	$V = s^3$
Volume of a cylinder	$V = \pi r^2 l$

1. A football field's playing area measures 100 yards by 55 yards. Each endzone is 10 yards deep. What's the total area of the field?

2. For mixing paint colors, Todd uses unmarked cylindrical measures. One cylinder is four inches in diameter and eight inches high. How much will it hold?

3. The park department recently planted petunias in six city parks. The beds were circular, and ten feet in diameter. If they planted nine petunias for every square foot, and the flowers cost $1.50 a dozen, how much did each petunia garden cost?

4. The park people then decided it would be nice to put tulip bulbs at four-inch intervals around the edges of these gardens. Tulip bulbs cost $30 per hundred. How much will it cost to plant tulips around all six flower beds?

5. The highway department wants to build a concrete retaining wall along a highway. It must be thirty feet long, two feet thick, and four feet high. How many cubic **yards** of concrete will it take to fill this space?

6. Todd knew a gallon is 231 cubic inches. He found a can $5\frac{1}{4}$ inches in diameter and five inches high. He knew by looking it wasn't big enough to hold a gallon of paint. What fractional part of a gallon would it hold?

7. Sue's garden is 72 feet long. She knows it contains 2,592 square feet. How wide is it?

8. What is the diameter of a cylindrical pipe that is eight feet long and contains 760.27 cubic feet?

NOW FOR TODD'S FISH PROBLEM

This problem has come up time and time again in this series. The reason for it is to demonstrate the "machinery" for solving a major portion of the algebra problems you will encounter.

Here it is once again in English.

A man caught a fish. Its head was nine inches long. Its body was equal to its head and half the tail. Its tail was as long as half the head plus the body.

O.K. Let's draw a picture of it.

(Well, it has three parts anyway.)

Fig. A.

Head = 9"

Body =

Tail =

The confusion comes because everything is stated in terms of something else. You have to get rid of some of the unknowns.

Since heads and parts of heads are easy to figure because we know the size of the head, let's try to get a comparison that uses only heads.

Look at this expression. Body =

If we could get rid of the "half tail," it would be easier to think about.

Fig. B.   Body = ◁ { ⊏⊐ } ← This can be substituted for half of this.

Tail = { ◿ + ☐ }

But half of this means half of **everything**.

Half of tail = ◿ + ▯

Fig. C.   Body = ◁ + { ◿ $\frac{1}{4}$ head ☐ half body }

It's still confusing because we have so many pieces of so many things. We must collect some of those pieces.

THINK OF **TWO** fish this size.

Fig. D.   2 bodies = ◁ + ◁ { ◿ + ☐ }

Now, you have bodies on both sides, and can subtract a body from each side. The equation will still balance.

Fig. E.   1 body = ◁ ◁ ◿

Body = $2\frac{1}{2}$ Heads $2\frac{1}{2} \times 9 = 22\frac{1}{2}$

B = $22\frac{1}{2}$

Now substitute this value in the expression that tells about the tail.

Fig. F.   Tail = ◿ + ☐

$\frac{1}{2}$ H = $4\frac{1}{2}$

$\underline{B = 22\frac{1}{2}}$

27

$$T = 27$$

$$\text{Fish} = H + B + T$$

$$\text{Fish} = 9 + 22\frac{1}{2} + 27$$

This pictorial demonstration may be the ultimate "james."

Todd solved the fish problem with algebra. Here is his method.

$$H = 9$$

$$B = H + \frac{T}{2}$$

$$T = \frac{H}{2} + B$$

Substitute

$$B = H + \frac{H + B}{2}$$

Multiply $\times$ 2

$$2B = 2H + \frac{H}{2} + B \text{ (This is Like Fig. C.)}$$

Subtract B

$$2B - B = 2H + \frac{H}{2} = B = 2H + \frac{H}{2} = B = 18 + 4\frac{1}{2} + B = 22\frac{1}{2}$$

Substitute

$$T = \frac{H}{2} + B = T = 4\frac{1}{2} + 22\frac{1}{2} + T = 27$$

$$\text{Fish} = 9 + 22\frac{1}{2} + 27 = 58\frac{1}{2}$$

If you remember this fish problem and solve it from time to time, you'll find it helps to keep your algebra skills sharp. Besides, you can use it to befuddle your friends.

VOCABULARY MATCHING (From the last five programs) (Answers on page 260.)

1. Absolute value

2. Zero

3. Negative number

4. Literal equation

5. Power

6. Square root

7. Constant

8. Variable

9. Hypotenuse

10. Right angle

11. Perimeter

12. Plane

13. Cube

14. Proportion

A. The unit used to measure volume.

B. The longest side of a right triangle.

C. $V = \pi r^2 l$

D. $\dfrac{2}{3} = \dfrac{8}{X}$

E. $\sqrt{}$

F. In geometry, a figure that has length and width but no depth.

G. 90°

H. The distance from zero.

I. $7^{\frac{4}{}}$

J. The number of swimming pools on the moon

K. $\underset{\frown}{4ab}$

L. A quantity less than zero.

M. The distance around something.

N. $\underset{\frown}{8\,mn}$

CUMULATIVE QUIZ (Answers on page 260.)

1. Martha bought a car for $7200. She traded in her present car for $2250. She also paid $850 cash. Express this transaction as an algebra problem. (Clue: Let X equal the amount she owes.)

2. Find the numbers expressed by these powers.

   A. 7^3

   B. 1.63×10^4

   C. 3^6

   D. 2.6×10^{-2}

3. Find the area of the shaded portion of these figures.

A.

D = 10"

B. 2 ft.

2 ft.

C.

4 ft.

5 ft.

D. 3 ft.

3 ft.

4. Todd knows 88 feet per second equal 60 miles per hour. But he's a law-abiding person and drives 55 miles per hour. How many feet per second is that?

5. Which is the better buy on laundry detergent, four pounds at 99¢, or six pounds at $1.50?

6. At a sale, Martha bought a dress that regularly sold for $5 more than twice what she paid for it. She paid $22. What would it have cost if it hadn't been on sale?

7. Todd and his family went to Canada on a vacation. He thought gas prices were too high until someone told him he was buying Imperial gallons, which are 1.2 times what U.S. gallons are. If Todd pays $1.40 per gallon at home, what is the most he can pay for an Imperial gallon and still break even?

8. How much would it cost to carpet a 12-foot by 12-foot room, if the carpet costs $14 per square yard?

9. The shadow of Bill's garage was 30 feet long. At the same time, the shadow cast by a five-foot fence post was $8\frac{1}{3}$ feet. How high is Bill's garage?

10. Martha was going to buy gifts for four friends. She found some cups and glass bowls she liked. She couldn't decide whether to buy one cup and three bowls, which would cost her $11, or one bowl and three cups for $9. Finally, she bought four bowls. How much did the four bowls cost?

STEVE WISE SAYS

REMEMBER:
The steps to "the James":

1. Draw a picture of it.

2. Assign the variables.

3. Work it first with easy numbers.

Proportion is a very valuable tool. Be certain you know about it.

Answers for Chapter 1

GOAL SETTING EXERCISES (pages 1-3)

1. **A.** $\frac{4}{8}$ or $\frac{1}{2}$ **B.** $\frac{5}{6}$ **C.** $\frac{3}{7}$ **D.** $\frac{4}{9}$

2.
$$0 \quad | \quad | \quad | \; | \quad 1 \quad\quad\quad\quad 2$$
$$\quad\ \ \frac{1}{4} \quad \frac{1}{2} \quad \frac{3}{4}\ \frac{7}{8}$$

3.
$$\frac{1}{4} = \frac{2}{8} = \frac{3}{12} = \frac{4}{16} = \frac{5}{20} = \frac{6}{24} = \frac{7}{28} = \frac{8}{32}$$

$$\frac{3}{8} = \frac{6}{16} = \frac{9}{24} = \frac{12}{32} = \frac{15}{40} = \frac{18}{48} = \frac{21}{56} = \frac{24}{64}$$

$$\frac{2}{3} = \frac{4}{6} = \frac{6}{9} = \frac{8}{12} = \frac{10}{15} = \frac{12}{18} = \frac{14}{21} = \frac{16}{24}$$

$$\frac{7}{8} = \frac{14}{16} = \frac{21}{24} = \frac{28}{32} = \frac{35}{40} = \frac{42}{48} = \frac{49}{56}$$

4. **A.** $\frac{2}{3}$ **B.** $*\frac{5}{5} = 1$ **C.** $*\frac{8}{8} = 1$ **D.** $\frac{5}{7}$

*Either answer is correct. The second answer is preferred because it has been reduced to lowest terms.

5. **A.** $*\frac{2}{4} = \frac{1}{2}$ **B.** $*\frac{2}{8} = \frac{1}{4}$ **C.** $*\frac{4}{8} = \frac{1}{2}$ **D.** $\frac{2}{16} = \frac{1}{8}$

6. **A.** $\frac{13}{15}$ **B.** $*\frac{29}{24} = 1\frac{5}{24}$ **C.** $\frac{23}{24}$ **D.** $*\frac{11}{8} = 1\frac{3}{8}$

7. $1\frac{1}{4}$ hr.

8. $\frac{1}{2}$ lb.

9. $1\frac{1}{4}$ gal.

10. **A.** 12   **B.** 24   **C.** 24

REACT, PRACTICE, AND EXTEND (pages 6-7)

1. **A.** $\dfrac{17}{20}$ **B.** $\dfrac{33}{28} = 1\dfrac{5}{28}$ **C.** $\dfrac{16}{15} = 1\dfrac{1}{15}$ **D.** $18\dfrac{5}{12}$

2. $\dfrac{1}{2} = \dfrac{2}{4} = \dfrac{3}{6} = \dfrac{4}{8} = \dfrac{5}{10}$

    $\dfrac{1}{4} = \dfrac{2}{8} = \dfrac{3}{12} = \dfrac{4}{16} = \dfrac{5}{20}$

    $\dfrac{1}{3} = \dfrac{2}{6} = \dfrac{3}{9} = \dfrac{4}{12} = \dfrac{5}{15}$

    $\dfrac{3}{8} = \dfrac{6}{16} = \dfrac{9}{24} = \dfrac{12}{32} = \dfrac{15}{40}$

    $\dfrac{5}{6} = \dfrac{10}{12} = \dfrac{15}{18} = \dfrac{20}{24} = \dfrac{25}{30}$

3. **A.** 3   **B.** $4\dfrac{5}{8}$ **C.** $\dfrac{13}{24}$ **D.** $\dfrac{16}{35}$

4. 1-D   5-B

    2-C   6-A

    3-E   7-G

    4-H   8-F

CUMULATIVE QUIZ (pages 9-10)

1. $\dfrac{2}{3} = \dfrac{16}{24}$
    $+\dfrac{7}{8} = \dfrac{21}{24}$
    $\dfrac{37}{24} = 1\dfrac{13}{24}$

2. $\dfrac{3}{5} = \dfrac{24}{40}$
    $+\dfrac{1}{8} = \dfrac{5}{40}$
    $\dfrac{29}{40}$

3. $\dfrac{5}{6} = \dfrac{35}{42}$
    $+\dfrac{2}{7} = \dfrac{12}{42}$
    $\dfrac{47}{42} = 1\dfrac{5}{42}$

4. $\dfrac{3}{8} = \dfrac{15}{40}$
    $+\dfrac{4}{5} = \dfrac{32}{40}$
    $\dfrac{47}{40} = 1\dfrac{7}{40}$

5. $\dfrac{2}{9} = \dfrac{4}{18}$
    $+\dfrac{5}{6} = \dfrac{15}{18}$
    $\dfrac{19}{18} = 1\dfrac{1}{18}$

6. $\dfrac{5}{7} = \dfrac{40}{56}$
    $+\dfrac{7}{8} = \dfrac{49}{56}$
    $\dfrac{89}{56} = 1\dfrac{33}{56}$

7.

$$\frac{6}{11} = \frac{12}{22}$$
$$+ \frac{3}{22} = \frac{3}{22}$$
$$\frac{15}{22}$$

8.

$$\frac{9}{14} = \frac{9}{14}$$
$$+ \frac{2}{7} = \frac{4}{14}$$
$$\frac{13}{14}$$

9.

$$\frac{2}{3} = \frac{16}{24}$$
$$- \frac{5}{8} = \frac{15}{24}$$
$$\frac{1}{24}$$

10.

$$\frac{3}{8} = \frac{21}{56}$$
$$- \frac{1}{7} = \frac{8}{56}$$
$$\frac{13}{56}$$

11.

$$\frac{7}{9} = \frac{7}{9}$$
$$- \frac{1}{3} = \frac{3}{9}$$
$$\frac{4}{9}$$

12.

$$\frac{5}{12} = \frac{5}{12}$$
$$- \frac{1}{6} = \frac{2}{12}$$
$$\frac{3}{12} = \frac{1}{4}$$

13.

$$\frac{7}{8} = \frac{63}{72}$$
$$- \frac{2}{9} = \frac{16}{72}$$
$$\frac{47}{72}$$

14.

$$\frac{3}{8} = \frac{6}{16}$$
$$- \frac{1}{4} = \frac{4}{16}$$
$$\frac{2}{16} = \frac{1}{8}$$

15.

$$\frac{4}{5} = \frac{28}{35}$$
$$- \frac{1}{7} = \frac{5}{35}$$
$$\frac{23}{35}$$

16.

$$\frac{9}{14} = \frac{9}{14}$$
$$- \frac{2}{7} = \frac{4}{14}$$
$$\frac{5}{14}$$

17.

$$1\frac{1}{3}$$
$$+ \quad \frac{2}{3}$$
$$1\frac{3}{3} = 2$$

18.

$$2\frac{1}{8} = 2\frac{5}{40}$$
$$+ 1\frac{4}{5} = 1\frac{32}{40}$$
$$3\frac{37}{40}$$

19.

$$3\frac{1}{2} = 3\frac{7}{14}$$
$$+ 1\frac{1}{7} = 1\frac{2}{14}$$
$$4\frac{9}{14}$$

20.

$$6\frac{1}{3} = 6\frac{3}{9}$$
$$+ 2\frac{1}{9} = 2\frac{1}{9}$$
$$8\frac{4}{9}$$

21.

$$3\frac{3}{4} = 3\frac{6}{8}$$
$$- 1\frac{1}{8} = 1\frac{1}{8}$$
$$2\frac{5}{8}$$

22.

$$4\frac{2}{3} = 4\frac{4}{6}$$
$$- \quad \frac{1}{6} = \quad \frac{1}{6}$$
$$4\frac{3}{6} = 4\frac{1}{2}$$

23.

$$4 \quad = 3\frac{8}{8}$$
$$- 1\frac{3}{8} = 1\frac{3}{8}$$
$$2\frac{5}{8}$$

24.

$$2\frac{1}{3} = 2\frac{8}{24} = 1\frac{32}{24}$$
$$- 1\frac{7}{8} = 1\frac{21}{24} = 1\frac{21}{24}$$
$$\frac{11}{24}$$

WORD PROBLEMS (pages 10-12)

1. $\dfrac{5}{8}$

2. 12

3. No. $\dfrac{1}{2} + \dfrac{1}{4} + \dfrac{1}{8} = \dfrac{7}{8}$ He still had $\dfrac{1}{8}$ to grade.

4. $5\dfrac{7}{8}$ miles

5. Todd is right. $\dfrac{7}{8} = \dfrac{14}{16}$ $\dfrac{14}{16} - \dfrac{13}{16} = \dfrac{1}{16}$

6. $8\dfrac{5}{24}$ tons

7. $1\dfrac{7}{8},$ $4\dfrac{3}{8},$ $2\dfrac{1}{2}$

8. $750. The fractions in this problem have nothing to do with the solution. Be careful that you use only the numbers you need to answer the question asked.

Answers for Chapter 2

GOAL SETTING EXERCISES (pages 17-19)

1. **A.** 3, 6, 9, 12, <u>15</u>, <u>18</u>, <u>21</u>, <u>24</u>   Add 3 each time.

   B. 4, 6, 5, 7, 6, 8, <u>7</u>, <u>9</u>, <u>8</u>, <u>10</u>   Add 2, then subtract 1.

   C. $\dfrac{1}{2}$ $\dfrac{5}{6}$ $\dfrac{21}{18}$ $\dfrac{81}{54}$ $\dfrac{297}{162}$ $\dfrac{1,053}{486}$ $\dfrac{3,645}{1,458}$ These fractions reduce to form this sequence:
   $\dfrac{3}{6}, \dfrac{5}{6}, \dfrac{7}{6}, \dfrac{9}{6}, \dfrac{11}{6}, \dfrac{13}{6}, \dfrac{15}{6}.$
   Add $\dfrac{1}{3}$ each time. Each denominator is 3 times the previous denominator.

   D. $1\dfrac{2}{3}$ $1\dfrac{11}{12}$ $1\dfrac{7}{12}$ $1\dfrac{5}{6}$ $1\dfrac{1}{2}$ $1\dfrac{3}{4}$ $1\dfrac{5}{12}$ $1\dfrac{2}{3}$ Add $\dfrac{1}{4}$, then subtract $\dfrac{1}{3}$.

2. **A.** $\dfrac{2}{3}$ **B.** $\dfrac{7}{12}$ **C.** $\dfrac{7}{6} = 1\dfrac{1}{6}$

3. **A.** 21 **B.** 24, 48, 96 (you'll probably have one of these) **C.** 35

4. As many as you want (infinite).

5. **A.** 14 − <u>1</u>, <u>2</u>, <u>7</u>, <u>14</u> **B.** 36 − <u>1</u>, <u>2</u>, <u>3</u>, <u>4</u>, <u>6</u>, <u>9</u>, <u>12</u>, <u>18</u>, <u>36</u>

   C. 17 − <u>1</u>, <u>17</u> **D.** 12 − <u>1</u>, <u>2</u>, <u>3</u>, <u>4</u>, <u>6</u>, <u>12</u>

6. 1. The identity elements for multiplication and subtraction are one and zero.

7. 3 (×) 2 (−) 1 (+) 0 (=) 5

8. **A.**
$$\begin{array}{r} \frac{1}{3} = \frac{4}{12} \\ + \frac{3}{4} = \frac{9}{12} \\ \hline \frac{13}{12} = 1\frac{1}{12} \end{array}$$
   B.
$$\begin{array}{r} \frac{2}{5} = \frac{6}{15} \\ + \frac{2}{3} = \frac{10}{15} \\ \hline \frac{16}{15} = 1\frac{1}{15} \end{array}$$

   C.
$$\begin{array}{r} \frac{3}{8} = \frac{9}{24} \\ + \frac{5}{6} = \frac{20}{24} \\ \hline \frac{29}{24} = 1\frac{5}{24} \end{array}$$
   D.
$$\begin{array}{r} \frac{1}{5} = \frac{6}{30} \\ + \frac{1}{6} = \frac{5}{30} \\ \hline \frac{11}{30} \end{array}$$

REACT, PRACTICE, AND EXTEND (pages 22-23)

Vocabulary Matching

1 - E   4 - A

2 - F   5 - B

3 - C   6 - D

1. **A.** $\dfrac{7}{12}$ **B.** $\dfrac{11}{12}$ **C.** $\dfrac{23}{40}$ **D.** $\dfrac{37}{40}$

    E. $\dfrac{45}{56}$ **F.** $\dfrac{44}{32} = 1\dfrac{12}{32} = 1\dfrac{3}{8}$ **G.** $\dfrac{95}{72} = 1\dfrac{23}{72}$ **H.** $\dfrac{32}{63}$

    I. $\dfrac{23}{45}$ **J.** $\dfrac{52}{32} = 1\dfrac{20}{32} = 1\dfrac{5}{8}$ **K.** $\dfrac{36}{35} = 1\dfrac{1}{35}$ **L.** $\dfrac{61}{45} = 1\dfrac{16}{45}$

2. **A.** $\dfrac{1}{12}$ **B.** $\dfrac{7}{40}$ **C.** $\dfrac{19}{30}$ **D.** $\dfrac{7}{30}$

    E. $\dfrac{2}{8} = \dfrac{1}{4}$ **F.** $\dfrac{19}{63}$ **G.** $\dfrac{11}{21}$ **H.** $\dfrac{23}{72}$

    I. $\dfrac{5}{21}$ **J.** $\dfrac{23}{48}$

3. $\dfrac{1}{9}, \dfrac{5}{16}, \dfrac{4}{9}, \dfrac{1}{2}, \dfrac{5}{8}, \dfrac{2}{3}, \dfrac{3}{4}, \dfrac{4}{5}, \dfrac{7}{8}$

4. $\dfrac{3}{4}$

CUMULATIVE QUIZ (pages 26-27)

1.
$$\begin{array}{r} \dfrac{2}{3} = \dfrac{16}{24} \\[2mm] + \dfrac{7}{8} = \dfrac{21}{24} \\[2mm] \hline \dfrac{37}{24} = 1\dfrac{13}{24} \end{array}$$

2.
$$\begin{array}{r} \dfrac{2}{9} = \dfrac{4}{18} \\[2mm] + \dfrac{5}{6} = \dfrac{15}{18} \\[2mm] \hline \dfrac{19}{18} = 1\dfrac{1}{18} \end{array}$$

3.
$$\begin{array}{r} \dfrac{3}{8} = \dfrac{21}{56} \\[2mm] - \dfrac{1}{7} = \dfrac{8}{56} \\[2mm] \hline \dfrac{13}{56} \end{array}$$

4. $\dfrac{2}{3} + \dfrac{3}{5} = \dfrac{19}{15} = 1\dfrac{4}{15}$

5. $\dfrac{2}{3} - \dfrac{5}{9} = \dfrac{3}{27} = \dfrac{1}{9}$

6. $\dfrac{2}{3} + \dfrac{6}{7} = \dfrac{32}{21} = 1\dfrac{11}{21}$

7. $\dfrac{2}{3} + \dfrac{1}{9} = \dfrac{21}{27} = \dfrac{7}{9}$

8. **A.** $\dfrac{1}{3}$ **B.** $\dfrac{1}{2}$ **C.** $\dfrac{1}{3}$ **D.** $4\dfrac{1}{7}$ **E.** $5\dfrac{1}{2}$

   F. $1\dfrac{4}{17}$ **G.** $\dfrac{1}{5}$ **H.** $1\dfrac{1}{3}$ **I.** $1\dfrac{3}{4}$ **J.** $12\dfrac{2}{3}$

9. $12\dfrac{23}{36}$

10. $193\dfrac{5}{8}$

CHALLENGE (page 27)

$$\frac{\triangle 2}{\boxed{3}} \;+\; \frac{\bigcirc 1}{\langle 4 \rangle} \;=\; \frac{\bigcirc 1 \;\; \bigcirc 1}{\bigcirc 1 \;\; \triangle 2}$$

Solution

Denominator

$$\boxed{3} \times \langle 4 \rangle = \bigcirc 1 \; \triangle 2$$

Numerator

$$\triangle 2 \times \boxed{4} = \oslash 8$$

$$\boxed{3} \times \bigcirc 1 = \boxed{3} \blacktriangleleft$$

$$\oslash 8 + \boxed{3} = \bigcirc 1 \; \bigcirc 1$$

The secret is identifying the identity element, $\bigcirc$.

$$\boxed{} \;\times\; \bigcirc \;=\; \boxed{}$$

The only thing you can multiply $\boxed{}$ by to get $\boxed{}$ is 1.

Answers for Chapter Three

GOAL SETTING EXERCISE (pages 30-32)

1.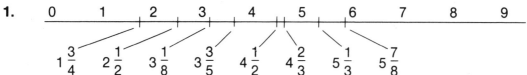

$$1\frac{3}{4} \quad 2\frac{1}{2} \quad 3\frac{1}{8} \quad 3\frac{3}{5} \quad 4\frac{1}{2} \quad 4\frac{2}{3} \quad 5\frac{1}{3} \quad 5\frac{7}{8}$$

2.
$$1\frac{3}{4} = \frac{7}{4} = \frac{14}{8} = \frac{21}{12} = \frac{28}{16} = \frac{35}{20} = \frac{42}{24} =$$

$$2\frac{1}{2} = \frac{5}{2} = \frac{10}{4} = \frac{15}{6} = \frac{20}{8} = \frac{25}{10} = \frac{30}{12} =$$

$$3\frac{3}{5} = \frac{18}{5} = \frac{36}{10} = \frac{54}{15} = \frac{72}{20} = \frac{90}{25} = \frac{108}{30} =$$

$$4\frac{1}{2} = \frac{9}{2} = \frac{18}{4} = \frac{27}{6} = \frac{36}{8} = \frac{45}{10} = \frac{54}{12} =$$

$$4\frac{2}{3} = \frac{14}{3} = \frac{28}{6} = \frac{42}{9} = \frac{56}{12} = \frac{70}{15} = \frac{84}{18} =$$

$$5\frac{1}{3} = \frac{16}{3} = \frac{32}{6} = \frac{48}{9} = \frac{64}{12} = \frac{80}{15} = \frac{96}{18} =$$

$$5\frac{7}{8} = \frac{47}{8} = \frac{94}{16} = \frac{141}{24} = \frac{188}{32} = \frac{235}{40} = \frac{282}{48} =$$

Note: There are many other possible answers. If yours differ greatly from these, you may still be right. Figure out what we did, and see if yours fit the pattern for rational families.

3. **A.** 9 and 11   **B.** 6 and 8   **C.** 4 and 5   **D.** 10 and 12

   E. 8 and 10   **F.** 10 and 11   **G.** 7 and 8

4. **A.** $\frac{9}{2}$ **B.** $\frac{20}{3}$ **C.** $\frac{15}{2}$ **D.** $\frac{9}{4}$ **E.** $\frac{63}{8}$ **F.** $\frac{27}{8}$ **G.** $\frac{50}{9}$ **H.** $\frac{19}{3}$ **I.** $\frac{79}{8}$ **J.** $\frac{32}{3}$ **K.** $\frac{49}{4}$

5. **A.** $2\frac{3}{4}$ **B.** $3\frac{2}{7}$ **C.** $5\frac{3}{4}$ **D.** 9   **E.** $4\frac{1}{2}$ **F.** 3

6. **A.**
$$2\frac{1}{2} = 2\frac{3}{6}$$
$$+\; 3\frac{1}{3} = 3\frac{2}{6}$$
$$\overline{\phantom{+\;3\frac{1}{3}} 5\frac{5}{6}}$$

   B.
$$7\frac{1}{2} = 7\frac{7}{14}$$
$$+\; 8\frac{2}{7} = 8\frac{4}{14}$$
$$\overline{\phantom{+\;8\frac{2}{7}} 15\frac{11}{14}}$$

   C.
$$9\frac{2}{5} = 9\frac{16}{40}$$
$$+\; 2\frac{3}{8} = 2\frac{15}{40}$$
$$\overline{\phantom{+\;2\frac{3}{8}} 11\frac{31}{40}}$$

   D.
$$7\frac{6}{7} = 7\frac{54}{63}$$
$$+\; 2\frac{1}{9} = 2\frac{7}{63}$$
$$\overline{\phantom{+\;2\frac{1}{9}} 9\frac{61}{63}}$$

7.

A.
$$4\frac{3}{4} = 4\frac{3}{4}$$
$$-\ 2\frac{1}{2} = 2\frac{2}{4}$$
$$2\frac{1}{4}$$

B.
$$7\frac{7}{8} = 7\frac{7}{8}$$
$$-\ 1\frac{3}{4} = 1\frac{6}{8}$$
$$6\frac{1}{8}$$

C.
$$2\frac{3}{8} = 2\frac{3}{8}$$
$$-\ 1\frac{1}{4} = 1\frac{2}{8}$$
$$1\frac{1}{8}$$

8.

A.
$$3\ \ = 2\frac{2}{2}$$
$$-\ 2\frac{1}{2} = 2\frac{1}{2}$$
$$\frac{1}{2}$$

B.
$$4\frac{1}{3} = 4\frac{5}{15} = 3\frac{20}{15}$$
$$-\ 2\frac{3}{5} = 2\frac{9}{15} = 2\frac{9}{15}$$
$$1\frac{11}{15}$$

C.
$$7\frac{1}{6} = 7\frac{4}{24} = 6\frac{28}{24}$$
$$-\ 3\frac{5}{8} = 3\frac{15}{24} = 3\frac{15}{24}$$
$$3\frac{13}{24}$$

9. $20\frac{7}{8}$

10. $10\frac{7}{8}$

REACT, PRACTICE, AND EXTEND (pages 34-35)

1.   **A.** 7   **B.** $7\frac{5}{8}$ **C.** $3\frac{1}{2}$ **D.** $1\frac{1}{2}$

2.   Answers will vary greatly.

3.   **A.** $4\frac{2}{3} = \frac{14}{3}$ **B.** $3\frac{7}{12} = \frac{43}{12}$ **C.** $4\frac{5}{9} = \frac{41}{9}$ **D.** $3\frac{7}{3} = 5\frac{1}{3}$ **E.** $2\frac{10}{4} = 4\frac{1}{2}$

4.
1 - C	2 - H	3 - D	4 - B
5 - F	6 - A	7 - E	8 - G

CUMULATIVE QUIZ (pages 38-40)

1.

A.
$$\frac{5}{7} = \frac{40}{56}$$
$$+\ \frac{7}{8} = \frac{49}{56}$$
$$\frac{89}{56} = 1\frac{33}{56}$$

B.
$$\frac{6}{11} = \frac{12}{22}$$
$$+\ \frac{3}{22} = \frac{3}{22}$$
$$\frac{15}{22}$$

C.
$$\frac{9}{14} = \frac{9}{14}$$
$$+\ \frac{2}{7} = \frac{4}{14}$$
$$\frac{13}{14}$$

D.
$$\frac{2}{3} = \frac{16}{24}$$
$$-\ \frac{5}{8} = \frac{15}{24}$$
$$\frac{1}{24}$$

E.
$$\frac{3}{8} = \frac{21}{56}$$
$$-\ \frac{1}{7} = \frac{8}{56}$$
$$\frac{13}{56}$$

F.
$$\frac{7}{8} = \frac{63}{72}$$
$$-\ \frac{2}{9} = \frac{16}{72}$$
$$\frac{47}{72}$$

2. **A.** $\dfrac{2}{3} + \dfrac{1}{4} = \dfrac{11}{12}$

B. $\dfrac{3}{8} + \dfrac{1}{5} = \dfrac{23}{40}$

C. $\dfrac{4}{5} + \dfrac{1}{8} = \dfrac{37}{40}$

D. $\dfrac{3}{4} + \dfrac{5}{8} = \dfrac{44}{32} = 1\dfrac{3}{8}$

E. $\dfrac{4}{9} + \dfrac{7}{8} = \dfrac{95}{72} = 1\dfrac{23}{72}$

F. $\dfrac{2}{7} + \dfrac{2}{9} = \dfrac{32}{63}$

3. **A.**
$$4\dfrac{2}{3} = 4\dfrac{4}{6}$$
$$+\ 3\dfrac{1}{2} = 3\dfrac{3}{6}$$
$$7\dfrac{7}{6} = 8\dfrac{1}{6}$$

B.
$$3\dfrac{1}{3} = 3\dfrac{8}{24}$$
$$+\ 2\dfrac{7}{8} = 2\dfrac{21}{24}$$
$$5\dfrac{29}{24} = 6\dfrac{5}{24}$$

C.
$$7\dfrac{3}{4} = 7\dfrac{27}{36}$$
$$+\ 1\dfrac{5}{9} = 1\dfrac{20}{36}$$
$$8\dfrac{47}{36} = 9\dfrac{11}{36}$$

D.
$$36\dfrac{4}{5} = 36\dfrac{32}{40}$$
$$+\ 22\dfrac{7}{8} = 22\dfrac{35}{40}$$
$$58\dfrac{67}{40} = 59\dfrac{27}{40}$$

E.
$$26\dfrac{4}{9} = 26\dfrac{28}{63}$$
$$+\ 3\dfrac{6}{7} = 3\dfrac{54}{63}$$
$$29\dfrac{82}{63} = 30\dfrac{19}{63}$$

F.
$$3\dfrac{5}{8} = 3\dfrac{5}{8}$$
$$+\ 2\dfrac{3}{4} = 2\dfrac{6}{8}$$
$$5\dfrac{11}{8} = 6\dfrac{3}{8}$$

G.
$$7\dfrac{2}{3} = 7\dfrac{4}{6}$$
$$+\ 5\dfrac{1}{2} = 5\dfrac{3}{6}$$
$$12\dfrac{7}{6} = 13\dfrac{1}{6}$$

H.
$$3\dfrac{7}{8}$$
$$+\ 2\dfrac{5}{8}$$
$$5\dfrac{12}{8} = 6\dfrac{1}{2}$$

4. **A.** $\dfrac{14}{3}$

B. $\dfrac{7}{2}$

C. $\dfrac{23}{8}$

D. $\dfrac{53}{8}$

E. $\dfrac{23}{7}$

F. $\dfrac{22}{3}$

G. $\dfrac{65}{4}$

H. $\dfrac{47}{9}$

I. $\dfrac{43}{10}$

J. $\dfrac{29}{11}$

5.   **A.** $3\frac{2}{3}$ **B.** $2\frac{2}{3}$ **C.** 3   **D.** $1\frac{2}{5}$ **E.** 3

F. $4\frac{2}{13}$ **G.** $3\frac{1}{2}$ **H.** $6\frac{1}{4}$ **I.** $5\frac{1}{2}$ **J.** $3\frac{2}{3}$

6.   **A.**
$$\begin{array}{r} 4\frac{4}{5} \\ -\ 2\frac{2}{5} \\ \hline 2\frac{2}{5} \end{array}$$

B.
$$\begin{array}{r} 3 = 2\frac{3}{3} \\ -\ 1\frac{1}{3} = 1\frac{1}{3} \\ \hline 1\frac{2}{3} \end{array}$$

C.
$$\begin{array}{r} 5\frac{2}{5} = 5\frac{18}{45} = 4\frac{63}{45} \\ -\ 1\frac{4}{9} = 1\frac{20}{45} = 1\frac{20}{45} \\ \hline 3\frac{43}{45} \end{array}$$

D.
$$\begin{array}{r} 6\frac{1}{2} = 6\frac{2}{4} = 5\frac{6}{4} \\ -\ 2\frac{3}{4} = 2\frac{3}{4} = 2\frac{3}{4} \\ \hline 3\frac{3}{4} \end{array}$$

E.
$$\begin{array}{r} 7\frac{1}{3} = 7\frac{4}{12} = 6\frac{16}{12} \\ -\ 6\frac{3}{4} = 6\frac{9}{12} = 6\frac{9}{12} \\ \hline 7\frac{7}{12} \end{array}$$

F.
$$\begin{array}{r} 2\frac{1}{8} = 2\frac{5}{40} = 1\frac{45}{40} \\ -\ \frac{9}{10} = \frac{36}{40} = \frac{36}{40} \\ \hline 1\frac{9}{40} \end{array}$$

G.
$$\begin{array}{r} 24\frac{1}{16} = 24\frac{1}{16} = 23\frac{17}{16} \\ -\ 3\frac{5}{8} = 3\frac{10}{16} = 3\frac{10}{16} \\ \hline 20\frac{7}{16} \end{array}$$

H.
$$\begin{array}{r} 14\frac{1}{5} = 14\frac{8}{40} = 13\frac{48}{40} \\ -\ 2\frac{3}{8} = 2\frac{15}{40} = 2\frac{15}{40} \\ \hline 11\frac{33}{40} \end{array}$$

7. $3\frac{1}{2} + 2\frac{1}{3} = 5\frac{5}{6}$ $\Bigg($ Proof:
$$\begin{array}{r} 5\frac{5}{6} = 5\frac{5}{6} \\ -\ 2\frac{1}{3} = 2\frac{2}{6} \\ \hline 3\frac{3}{6} = 3\frac{1}{2} \end{array}\Bigg)$$

8.

$$8\frac{1}{2} = 8\frac{2}{4}$$
$$6\frac{3}{4} = 6\frac{3}{4}$$
$$6\frac{3}{4} = 6\frac{3}{4}$$
$$+\ 1\frac{1}{4} = 1\frac{1}{4}$$
$$21\frac{9}{4} = 23\frac{1}{4}$$

9.

$$\frac{350}{6} = 6\ \overline{)350}\ \ \frac{58}{} = 58\frac{1}{3}$$
$$\underline{30}$$
$$50$$
$$\underline{48}$$
$$2$$

They'll probably want to bring 59 pies, though. It's not likely that someone can bake a third of a pie.

10.

$$\frac{3}{4} + \frac{3}{4} = 1\frac{1}{2} + 1\frac{1}{2} = 3$$

$$\begin{array}{r} 4 \\ -\ 3 \\ \hline 1 \end{array}$$ the remaining piece is 1 ft. by 8 ft.

Remaining →

$$2\ \frac{3}{4} \times 1\ \text{ft.}$$

← $$2\ \ 1 \times 4\ \text{ft.}$$

11.

$$\begin{array}{r} 2\frac{1}{2} \\ 2\frac{1}{2} \\ +\ \\ +\ 2\frac{1}{2} \\ \hline 7\frac{1}{2} \end{array}$$
$$\begin{array}{r} 3\frac{3}{4} \\ +\ 3\frac{3}{4} \\ \hline 7\frac{1}{2} \end{array}$$
$$\begin{array}{r} 7\frac{1}{2} \\ +\ 7\frac{1}{2} \\ \hline 15 \end{array}$$

12. Yes, he'd have enough. Two gallons = $\begin{array}{r} 16 \\ -\ 15 \\ \hline 1 \end{array}$ pints

1 pint remaining

EXTENDING YOUR UNDERSTANDING (page 41)

1. Fooled you; $1\frac{1}{2}$ hour and 90 minutes are the same thing.

Answers for Chapter Four

GOAL SETTING EXERCISE (pages 42-44)

1. $\frac{1}{16}, \frac{1}{8}, \frac{3}{16}, \frac{1}{4}, \frac{5}{16}, \frac{3}{8}, \frac{7}{16}, \frac{1}{2}, \frac{9}{16}, \frac{5}{8}, \frac{11}{16}, \frac{3}{4}, \frac{13}{16}, \frac{7}{8}, \frac{15}{16},$ 1

2. $\frac{4}{5}$ shaded $\frac{7}{9}$ shaded

   $\frac{3}{12}$ shaded $\frac{5}{15}$ shaded

3. **A.** $\dfrac{\star\star\star}{\star\star\star\star\star\star\star}$ **B.** $\dfrac{\star\star\star\star}{\star\star\star\star\star}$ **C.** $\dfrac{\star\star\star\star\star\star\star}{\star\star\star\star\star\star\star\star\star}$ **D.** $\dfrac{\star\star}{\star\star\star\star\star}$

   E. $\dfrac{\star\star\star}{\star\star\star\star\star\star\star\star\star\star\star\star\star\star\star}$ **F.** $\dfrac{\star\star\star}{\star\star\star\star\star\star\star\star\star}$ **G.** $\dfrac{\star\star\star\star\star}{\star\star\star\star\star\star\star\star\star\star}$

   H. $\dfrac{\star\star\star\star\star\star\star\star}{\star\star\star\star\star\star\star\star\star\star\star\star}$

4. **A.** $\dfrac{3}{9} = \dfrac{\star}{\star\star\star}$ **B.** $\dfrac{5}{10} = \dfrac{\star}{\star\star}$ **C.** $\dfrac{8}{12} = \dfrac{\star\star}{\star\star\star}$

5. **A.** $\dfrac{(2)}{(3)} \ \dfrac{6}{9}, \ \dfrac{8}{12}, \ \dfrac{10}{15}, \ \dfrac{12}{18}, \ \dfrac{14}{21}, \ \dfrac{16}{24}$

   B. $\dfrac{(3)}{(5)} \ \dfrac{6}{10}, \ \dfrac{9}{15}, \ \dfrac{12}{20}, \ \dfrac{15}{25}, \ \dfrac{21}{35}$

   C. $\dfrac{(5)}{(8)} \ \dfrac{10}{16}, \ \dfrac{20}{32}, \ \dfrac{30}{48}, \ \dfrac{35}{56}$

6. $7\frac{1}{2} + 4\frac{1}{5} - 1\frac{1}{3} = 10\frac{11}{30}$

7. **A.** $\dfrac{9}{16}$ **B.** $\dfrac{3}{8}$ **C.** $\dfrac{7}{12}$ **D.** $\dfrac{11}{18}$

8. A. $4\dfrac{1}{3} = 4\dfrac{5}{15} = 3\dfrac{20}{15}$

$-\ 2\dfrac{4}{5} = 2\dfrac{12}{15} = 2\dfrac{12}{15}$

$1\dfrac{8}{15}$

B. $6\dfrac{1}{3} = 6\dfrac{2}{6} = 5\dfrac{8}{6}$

$-\ 2\dfrac{1}{2} = 2\dfrac{3}{6} = 2\dfrac{3}{6}$

$3\dfrac{5}{6}$

REACT, PRACTICE, AND EXTEND (pages 47-50)

1. A. 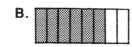   **B.**    **C.**

2. A. $\dfrac{1}{2}$ **B.** $\dfrac{1}{4}$ **C** $\dfrac{1}{4}$

3. A.

B.

C.

4. Those of the same family are A, C, D, E, and F.

5. A. $4 + 5 + \dfrac{1}{3} + \dfrac{1}{2} = 9\dfrac{5}{6}$

B. $7 + 2 + 3 = 12$

$\dfrac{1}{2} + \dfrac{1}{4} + \dfrac{3}{8} = \dfrac{4}{8} + \dfrac{2}{8} + \dfrac{3}{8} = \dfrac{9}{8} = 1\dfrac{1}{8}$

12

$+\ 1\dfrac{1}{8}$

$13\dfrac{1}{8}$

C. $4 - 3 = 1$

$\dfrac{7}{8} - \dfrac{5}{12} = \dfrac{84}{96} - \dfrac{40}{96} = \dfrac{44}{96} = \dfrac{11}{24}$

$1\dfrac{11}{24}$

6. $\dfrac{22}{7},\ \dfrac{44}{14},\ \dfrac{66}{21},\ \dfrac{88}{28},\ \dfrac{110}{35},\ \dfrac{132}{42},\ \dfrac{154}{49},\ \dfrac{176}{56},\ \dfrac{198}{63},\ \dfrac{220}{70}$

7.

0    $\dfrac{22}{7}$ All the members of a fraction family "stack up" at one point or a number line.

A.

$\underline{7}$	$\underline{22}$
$\underline{35}$	$\underline{110}$
$\underline{49}$	$\underline{154}$
$\underline{35}$	$\underline{110}$
$\underline{14}$	$\underline{44}$
$\underline{21}$	$\underline{66}$
$\underline{63}$	$\underline{198}$
$\underline{28}$	$\underline{88}$

B.

$\underline{9}$	$\underline{22}$ & $\underline{44}$
$\underline{26}$	$\underline{66}$ & $\underline{88}$
$\underline{51}$	$\underline{154}$ & $\underline{176}$
$\underline{36}$	$\underline{110}$ & $\underline{132}$
$\underline{12}$	$\underline{22}$ & $\underline{44}$

VOCABULARY (page 51)

1. Infinity

2. Numerator

3. Mixed number

4. Inverse operation

5. Denominator

6. Fraction family

7. Lowest terms

8. Number line

9. Identity element

10. Common denominator

CUMULATIVE QUIZ (pages 52-54)

1. A. $1\frac{1}{18}$ B. $1\frac{33}{56}$ C. $\frac{15}{22}$ D. $\frac{13}{14}$ E. $\frac{1}{24}$ F. $\frac{13}{56}$ G. $\frac{4}{9}$ H. $\frac{1}{4}$

2. A. $\frac{1}{3}$ B. $\frac{1}{2}$ C. $\frac{1}{3}$ D. $4\frac{1}{7}$ E. $5\frac{1}{2}$ F. 3 G. $12\frac{2}{3}$

3. A.
$$4\frac{2}{3} = 4\frac{4}{6}$$
$$+\ 3\frac{1}{2} = 3\frac{3}{6}$$
$$7\frac{7}{6} = 8\frac{1}{6}$$

B.
$$3\frac{1}{3} = 3\frac{8}{24}$$
$$+\ 2\frac{7}{8} = 2\frac{21}{24}$$
$$5\frac{29}{24} = 6\frac{5}{24}$$

C.
$$7\frac{3}{4} = 7\frac{27}{36}$$
$$+\ 1\frac{5}{9} = 1\frac{20}{36}$$
$$8\frac{47}{36} = 9\frac{11}{36}$$

D.
$$36\frac{4}{5} = 36\frac{32}{40}$$
$$+22\frac{7}{8} = 22\frac{35}{40}$$
$$58\frac{67}{40} = 59\frac{27}{40}$$

E.
$$26\frac{4}{9} = 26\frac{28}{63}$$
$$+\ 3\frac{6}{7} = 3\frac{54}{63}$$
$$29\frac{82}{63} = 30\frac{19}{63}$$

4. Change these mixed numbers to improper fractions.

A. $5\frac{6}{7} = \frac{41}{7}$ B. $3\frac{3}{7} = \frac{24}{7}$ C. $2\frac{2}{9} = \frac{20}{9}$ D. $5\frac{7}{8} = \frac{47}{8}$ E. $6\frac{3}{4} = \frac{27}{4}$

F. $17 = \frac{17}{1}$ G. $24\frac{1}{6} = \frac{145}{6}$ H. $15\frac{1}{3} = \frac{46}{3}$ I. $16\frac{1}{8} = \frac{129}{8}$ J. $14\frac{1}{2} = \frac{29}{2}$

5. A.
$$7 \qquad 6\frac{7}{7}$$
$$-\ 3\frac{1}{7} = 3\frac{1}{7}$$
$$3\frac{6}{7}$$

B.
$$8\frac{4}{5} = 8\frac{12}{15}$$
$$-\ 2\frac{1}{3} = 2\frac{5}{15}$$
$$6\frac{7}{15}$$

C.
$$6\frac{1}{3} = 6\frac{8}{24} = 5\frac{32}{24}$$
$$-\ 2\frac{5}{8} = 2\frac{15}{24} = 2\frac{15}{24}$$
$$3\frac{17}{24}$$

D. $9\dfrac{7}{8} = 9\dfrac{14}{16} = 8\dfrac{30}{16}$

$-\;2\dfrac{15}{16} = 2\dfrac{15}{16} = 2\dfrac{15}{16}$

$\qquad\qquad\qquad\qquad\; 6\dfrac{15}{16}$

6. **A.** $2\dfrac{1}{3} = 1\dfrac{20}{15}$ **B.** $3\dfrac{1}{8} = 3\dfrac{1}{8} = 2\dfrac{9}{8}$

$\qquad -1\dfrac{3}{5} = 1\dfrac{9}{15}$ $-1\dfrac{3}{4} = 1\dfrac{6}{8} = 1\dfrac{6}{8}$

$\qquad\qquad\quad\;\; \dfrac{11}{15}$ $1\dfrac{3}{8}$

7. 1

8. 3 gallon cans, 2 half-gallon cans, 1 quart can, and 6 pint cans

9. Sue is 33, and her sister is $28\dfrac{1}{2}$

10. $\dfrac{15}{26}$ **women;** $\dfrac{11}{26}$ **men**

11. 3 miles

EXTENDING YOUR UNDERSTANDING (page 54)

1. **A.** $\dfrac{1}{2} + \dfrac{2}{3} + \dfrac{3}{4} = 1\dfrac{11}{12}$ **B.** $\dfrac{1}{2} + \dfrac{2}{3} - \dfrac{3}{4} = \dfrac{5}{12}$ **C.** $\dfrac{1}{2} - \dfrac{2}{3} + \dfrac{3}{4} = \dfrac{7}{12}$

Note - on the last one it is easier to think about if you add $\dfrac{2}{3} + \dfrac{3}{4}$ first, and subtract $\dfrac{1}{2}$. In a problem that includes both addition and subtraction, the order in which you do the operations makes no difference.

2. Yes

3. They are called compound fractions. It would be like $3\dfrac{1}{2}$ things shared by 4 people. The next member would be $\dfrac{7}{8}$.

Answers for Chapter Five

GOAL SETTING EXERCISE (pages 57-59)

1. **A.** $\frac{1}{6}$ **B.** $\frac{1}{2}$ **C.** $\frac{5}{28}$ **D.** $\frac{16}{45}$

2. **A.** $2\frac{1}{2}$ **B.** $4\frac{1}{2}$ **C.** $3\frac{1}{2}$ **D.** 5

3. **A.** $1\frac{2}{3}$ **B.** 1 **C.** $3\frac{6}{7}$ **D.** $2\frac{11}{12}$

4. **A.** $6\frac{1}{4}$ **B.** $8\frac{1}{3}$ **C.** $22\frac{2}{3}$ **D.** $11\frac{2}{3}$

5. **A.** 28 **B.** 36 **C.** 10 **D.** 60

6. **A.** $1\frac{7}{9}$ **B.** 18 **C.** $1\frac{11}{15}$ **D.** $1\frac{13}{22}$

7. 24

8. $\frac{7}{16}$

9. 5 in the first truck, $2\frac{1}{2}$ in the second

10. $18\frac{2}{3}$

REACT, PRACTICE, AND EXTEND (pages 63-64)

1. **A.** $\frac{1}{6}$ **B.** $\frac{7}{32}$ **C.** $\frac{1}{2}$ **D.** $\frac{21}{32}$ **E.** $\frac{2}{5}$ **F.** $\frac{8}{21}$

2. **A.** $1\frac{1}{2}$ **B.** $2\frac{2}{5}$ **C.** 4 **D.** $\frac{5}{7}$ **E.** $2\frac{4}{7}$ **F.** $2\frac{1}{2}$

3. **A.** $2\frac{1}{24}$ **B.** $\frac{7}{8}$ **C.** $\frac{21}{125}$ **D.** $\frac{28}{45}$ **E.** $\frac{25}{64}$ **F.** $\frac{57}{64}$

4. **A.** $5\frac{1}{4}$ **B.** $9\frac{1}{2}$ **C.** $7\frac{1}{8}$

5. **A.** $1\frac{2}{7}$ **B.** $3\frac{1}{2}$ **C.** $1\frac{3}{5}$

6. **A.** 8 **B.** $4\frac{1}{6}$ **C.** $4\frac{8}{33}$

7. $6\frac{2}{3}$

VOCABULARY STUDY (page 64)

Multiplicand times the **multiplier** equals the **product.**

Dividend divided by the **divisor** equals the **quotient.**

One-half of the **multiplicand** equals the **product.**

The quotient times the **divisor** equals the dividend.

The product divided by the multiplicand equals the **multiplier.**

CUMULATIVE QUIZ (page 64)

1. **A.** $\frac{13}{15}$ **B.** $1\frac{7}{40}$ **C.** $2\frac{10}{21}$

2. **A.** $\frac{5}{12}$ **B.** $\frac{3}{40}$ **C.** $2\frac{7}{20}$

3. **A.** $\frac{1}{4}$ **B.** $1\frac{3}{5}$ **C.** $13\frac{1}{3}$

4.   A. $10\frac{1}{2}$ **B.** $61\frac{2}{3}$ **C.** $\frac{3}{185}$

WORD PROBLEMS (page 65)

1. 10

2. 96

3. $320.00

4. 96

5. $4.32

6. Sue $1\frac{1}{12}$, Todd $6\frac{1}{2}$, Bill $4\frac{7}{8}$

7. The math answer is $6\frac{6}{7}$, **but** the real answer is 6. Costumes are very much like "piles." Either you have one or you don't.

8. $7\frac{1}{2}$

EXTENDING YOUR SKILLS (pages 66-67)

1. $4\frac{1}{2} \times \frac{2}{3} = 3$ $4\frac{1}{2} \times \frac{1}{3}$

$0 \times \frac{2}{3}$ $1 \times \frac{2}{3}$ $2 \times \frac{2}{3}$ $3 \times \frac{2}{3}$ $4 \times \frac{2}{3}$ $5 \times \frac{2}{3}$ $6 \times \frac{2}{3}$ $7 \times \frac{2}{3}$ $8 \times \frac{2}{3}$ $9 \times \frac{2}{3}$

Times $\frac{2}{3}$

0   1   2   3   4   5   6

2. $5\frac{1}{3} \times \frac{3}{4} = 4$ $5\frac{1}{3} \times \frac{3}{4}$

$0 \times \frac{3}{4}$ $1 \times \frac{3}{4}$ $2 \times \frac{3}{4}$ $3 \times \frac{3}{4}$ $4 \times \frac{3}{4}$ $5 \times \frac{3}{4}$ $6 \times \frac{3}{4}$

Times $\frac{3}{4}$

0   1   2   3   4   5

3. $$\frac{3\frac{1}{3}}{5} = \frac{6\frac{2}{3}}{10} = \frac{10}{15}$$

4. $$\frac{2\frac{1}{7}}{4} = \frac{4\frac{2}{7}}{8} = \frac{6\frac{3}{7}}{12} = \frac{8\frac{4}{7}}{16} = \frac{10\frac{5}{7}}{20} = \frac{12\frac{6}{7}}{24} = \frac{14\frac{7}{7}}{28} \text{ or } \frac{15}{28}$$

5. $$\frac{5\frac{3}{4}}{8} = \frac{11\frac{1}{2}}{16} = \frac{17\frac{1}{4}}{24} = \frac{23}{32}$$

Answers for Chapter Six

GOAL SETTING EXERCISE (pages 69-71)

1. **A.** $\frac{3}{8}$ **B.** $\frac{7}{32}$ **C.** $\frac{1}{4}$ **D.** $\frac{2}{3}$ **E.** 3   **F.** $5\frac{5}{12}$

2. **A.** 6   **B.** 8   **C.** $11\frac{1}{5}$ **D.** $\frac{3}{32}$ **E.** $5\frac{5}{16}$ **F.** $1\frac{1}{2}$

3. **A.** $\frac{\overset{1}{\cancel{3}}}{\underset{1}{\cancel{4}}} \times \frac{\overset{2}{\cancel{8}}}{\underset{3}{\cancel{9}}} = \frac{2}{3}$ **B.** $\frac{\overset{1}{\cancel{2}}}{3} \times \frac{1}{\underset{2}{\cancel{4}}} = \frac{1}{6}$ **C.** $\frac{\overset{1}{\cancel{5}}}{\underset{4}{\cancel{8}}} \times \frac{\overset{1}{\cancel{2}}}{\underset{3}{\cancel{15}}} = \frac{1}{12}$

   D. $\frac{\overset{1}{\cancel{5}}}{\underset{2}{\cancel{8}}} \times \frac{\overset{1}{\cancel{4}}}{\underset{1}{\cancel{5}}} = \frac{1}{2}$ **E.** $\frac{\overset{1}{\cancel{7}}}{\underset{3}{\cancel{9}}} \times \frac{\overset{1}{\cancel{3}}}{\underset{2}{\cancel{14}}} = \frac{1}{6}$ **F.** $\frac{\overset{1}{\cancel{5}}}{\underset{3}{\cancel{6}}} \times \frac{\overset{2}{\cancel{4}}}{\underset{3}{\cancel{15}}} = \frac{2}{9}$

4. **A.** $\frac{2\frac{1}{2}}{\frac{1}{3}} = \frac{5}{\frac{2}{3}} = \frac{7\frac{1}{2}}{\frac{3}{3}} = \frac{10}{\frac{4}{3}}$ **B.** $\frac{5}{\frac{8}{2}{3}} = \frac{10}{\frac{8}{4}{3}} = \frac{15}{\frac{8}{6}{3}} = \frac{20}{\frac{8}{8}{3}} = \frac{25}{\frac{8}{10}{3}}$ **C.** $\frac{7\frac{1}{2}}{100} = \frac{15}{200}$

5. 14

6. $16 \div \frac{2}{3} = \frac{16}{1} \times \frac{3}{2} = \frac{48}{2} = 24$ Check: $\frac{16}{24} = \frac{2}{3}$

7. An easy solution to this problem is a compound fraction family.

   $\frac{\frac{3}{4}}{\frac{1}{3}} = \frac{\frac{6}{4}}{\frac{2}{3}} = \frac{\frac{9}{4}}{\frac{3}{3}}$ 9 quarters   Answer: 9 quarters in 1 hour

   1 hour

REACT, PRACTICE, AND EXTEND (pages 73-75)

1. **A.** $\frac{1}{4}$ **B.** $\frac{4}{7}$ **C.** $\frac{1}{6}$ **D.** $\frac{3}{8}$ **E.** $\frac{1}{10}$ **F.** $\frac{1}{10}$

2. **A.** 12 **B.** 2 **C.** 4 **D.** 10 **E.** 14 **F.** 1

3. **A.** $\frac{2}{3} \times \frac{3}{4} = \frac{3}{3} \times \frac{2}{4} = \frac{1}{2}$ **B.** $\frac{5}{8} \times \frac{2}{5} = \frac{2}{8} \times \frac{5}{5} = \frac{1}{4}$

 C. $\frac{3}{4} \times \frac{4}{5} = \frac{4}{4} \times \frac{3}{5} = \frac{3}{5}$ **D.** $\frac{7}{9} \times \frac{5}{7} = \frac{5}{9} \times \frac{7}{7} = \frac{5}{9}$

 E. $\frac{11}{14} \times \frac{7}{11} = \frac{7}{14} \times \frac{11}{11} = \frac{1}{2}$ **F.** $\frac{6}{15} \times \frac{5}{6} = \frac{6}{6} \times \frac{5}{15} = \frac{1}{3}$

4. **A.** $\frac{1}{2}$ **B.** $\frac{2}{1}$ **C.** $\frac{4}{3}$ **D.** $\frac{3}{16}$ **E.** $\frac{8}{1}$ **F.** $\frac{1}{9}$ **G.** $\frac{2}{3}$ **H.** $\frac{1}{6}$ **I.** $\frac{15}{31}$ **J.** $\frac{67}{1}$

VOCABULARY MATCHING (page 76)

1. C   **5.** H

2. A   **6.** D

3. F   **7.** B

4. E   **8.** G

CUMULATIVE QUIZ (pages 76-78)

1. **A.** $2\frac{1}{2}$ **B.** $4\frac{17}{24}$ **C.** $7\frac{1}{12}$ **D.** $10\frac{13}{24}$ **E.** $6\frac{13}{40}$ **F.** $11\frac{1}{20}$

2. **A.** $\frac{13}{24}$ **B.** $\frac{2}{9}$ **C.** $\frac{2}{21}$ **D.** $2\frac{11}{24}$ **E.** $\frac{5}{16}$ **F.** $\frac{1}{16}$

3. **A.** $8\frac{1}{3}$ **B.** $4\frac{1}{16}$ **C.** $3\frac{1}{9}$ **D.** $1\frac{11}{15}$ **E.** $19\frac{1}{5}$ **F.** $1\frac{7}{8}$ **G.** $\frac{4}{15}$ **H.** $9\frac{1}{3}$

4. **A.** $\frac{1}{3} \times 36 = 12$ **B.** $7 \div \frac{1}{3} = 21$ **C.** $4\frac{1}{2} \times \frac{1}{12} = \frac{3}{8}$

5. 18

6. 27

7. David is 30. When Jimmy is half David's age, Jimmy will be 25 and David 50.

8. 24

9. 64

10. $1\frac{1}{8}$ million

EXTENDING YOUR UNDERSTANDING (page 78)

1.
$$\frac{3}{4} = \frac{3\frac{3}{4}}{5} = \frac{4\frac{1}{2}}{6} = \frac{5\frac{1}{4}}{7} = \frac{6}{8} = \frac{6\frac{3}{4}}{9} = \frac{7\frac{1}{2}}{10} = \frac{8\frac{1}{4}}{11} = \frac{9}{12}$$

2.
$$\frac{5}{6} = \frac{5\frac{5}{6}}{7} = \frac{6\frac{2}{3}}{8} = \frac{7\frac{1}{2}}{9} = \frac{8\frac{1}{3}}{10} = \frac{9\frac{1}{6}}{11} = \frac{10}{12}$$

3.
$$\frac{2}{3} = \frac{2\frac{2}{3}}{4} = \frac{3\frac{1}{3}}{5} = \frac{4}{6} = \frac{4\frac{2}{3}}{7} = \frac{5\frac{1}{3}}{8} = \frac{6}{9} = \frac{6\frac{2}{3}}{10}$$

Answers for Chapter Seven

GOAL SETTING EXERCISE (pages 81-83)

1. **A.** .25 **B.** .75 **C.** .80 **D.** $.66\frac{2}{3}$ **E.** $.87\frac{1}{2}$ **F.** $.83\frac{1}{3}$

2. **A.** $\frac{2}{5}$ **B.** $\frac{3}{4}$ **C.** $\frac{7}{50}$ **D.** $\frac{3}{8}$ **E.** $\frac{1}{25}$ **F.** $\frac{1}{6}$

3.

A.
$$\begin{array}{r} 23.04 \\ +\ 2.3 \\ \hline 25.34 \end{array}$$

B.
$$\begin{array}{r} 7.5 \\ +14.006 \\ \hline 21.506 \end{array}$$

C.
$$\begin{array}{r} 25.000 \\ +\ 2.372 \\ \hline 27.372 \end{array}$$

D.
$$\begin{array}{r} 17.6 \\ +\ .004 \\ \hline 17.604 \end{array}$$

E.
$$\begin{array}{r} 23.33\frac{1}{3} \\ +\ 6.66\frac{2}{3} \\ \hline 30.000 \end{array}$$

F.
$$\begin{array}{r} 2.46 \\ +21.50 \\ \hline 23.96 \end{array}$$

4.

A.
$$\begin{array}{r} 26.21 \\ -12.04 \\ \hline 14.17 \end{array}$$

B.
$$\begin{array}{r} 17.563 \\ -\ 3.4 \\ \hline 14.163 \end{array}$$

C.
$$\begin{array}{r} 22.003 \\ -\ 1.25 \\ \hline 20.753 \end{array}$$

D.
$$\begin{array}{r} 14.000 \\ -\ 6.936 \\ \hline 7.064 \end{array}$$

E.
$$\begin{array}{r} 24.030 \\ -14.406 \\ \hline 9.624 \end{array}$$

F.
$$\begin{array}{r} 5.040 \\ -\ 5.004 \\ \hline .036 \end{array}$$

5.

A.
$$\begin{array}{r} 22.6 \\ \times 2.06 \\ \hline 1356 \\ 4520 \\ \hline 46.556 \end{array}$$

B.
$$\begin{array}{r} 12.4 \\ \times .003 \\ \hline .0372 \end{array}$$

C.
$$\begin{array}{r} 26.1 \\ \times\ 2.4 \\ \hline 1044 \\ 522 \\ \hline 62.64 \end{array}$$

D.
$$\begin{array}{r} 14.36 \\ \times\ 1.4 \\ \hline 5744 \\ 1436 \\ \hline 20.104 \end{array}$$

E.
$$\begin{array}{r} 2.48 \\ \times 2.48 \\ \hline 1984 \\ 992 \\ 496 \\ \hline 6.1504 \end{array}$$

F.
$$\begin{array}{r} 17. \\ \times\ 2.5 \\ \hline 85 \\ 34 \\ \hline 42.5 \end{array}$$

6.

A.
$$.04\overline{)\ .24}\quad 6.$$

B.
$$2.5\overline{)\ 38.00}\quad 15.2$$
$$\begin{array}{r} 25 \\ \hline 130 \\ 125 \\ \hline 50 \\ 50 \\ \hline 0 \end{array}$$

C.
$$.33\overline{)\ 44.0000}\quad 133.33\frac{1}{3}$$
$$\begin{array}{r} 33 \\ \hline 110 \\ 99 \\ \hline 110 \\ 99 \\ \hline 110 \\ 99 \\ \hline 110 \\ 99 \\ \hline 11 \end{array}$$

D.
$$14\overline{)\ .28}\quad .02$$

E.
$$1.3\overline{)\ 2.6}\quad 2.$$

F.
$$2.2\overline{)\ .660}\quad .3$$
$$\begin{array}{r} 66 \\ \hline 000 \end{array}$$

7. .25

8. 1311.7

9. $70.00

10. Decorations $240.00
     Utilities $ 80.00
     Janitor $ 90.00
     Food $330.00
     Entertainment $260.00

REACT, PRACTICE, AND EXTEND (pages 88-90)

1. **A.** $.33\frac{1}{3}$ **B.** $.77\frac{7}{9}$ **C.** $.90\frac{10}{11}$ **D.** $.78\frac{4}{7}$ **E.** $.87\frac{1}{2}$

2. **A.** 3.34   **B.** 5.684   **C.** 30   **D.** 68.7   **E.** 100   **F.** 40.55

3. **A.** 3.63   **B.** 2.104   **C.** 1.73   **D.** 266.397   **E.** 2.7   **F.** 14.7

4. **A.** .092   **B.** 44.46   **C.** .09168   **D.** .1512   **E.** 1.86   **F.** .0042

5. **A.** $.17\frac{9}{13}$ or .1769   **B.** 68   **C.** $15.78\frac{18}{19}$ or 15.79

   D. 300   **E.** $102.12\frac{36}{47}$ or 102.128   **F.** 2

6. **A.** 35%   **B.** 780%   **C.** 6%   **D.** 123%   **E.** 3.5%   **F.** 25%

7. **A.** .43   **B.** .576   **C.** $.87\frac{1}{2}$ or .875   **D.** .044

   E. .05   **F.** 1.63   **G.** .0003   **H.** .5

8. 72.9

9. 32.1

10. 66.25

11.   .2328

CUMULATIVE QUIZ (pages 91-93)

1.   **A.** $\dfrac{3}{32}$ **B.** $1\dfrac{1}{6}$ **C.** $1\dfrac{1}{2}$ **D.** $4\dfrac{3}{8}$ **E.** $\dfrac{11}{24}$ **F.** $3\dfrac{2}{5}$

2.   **A.** 7.88   **B.** 9.3   **C.** 11   **D.** 7.406   **E.** 7.85   **F.** 10

3.   **A.** 1.47   **B.** 15.61   **C.** 1.1   **D.** 2.68   **E.** .3   **F.** .008

4.   **A.** 10.188   **B.** .0414   **C.** 21.9912

5.   **A.** 11   **B.** .858   **C.** .06888

6.   20

7.   .237

8.   **A.** $\dfrac{1}{100}$ **B.** $\dfrac{1}{20}$ **C.** $\dfrac{1}{10}$ **D.** $\dfrac{1}{4}$ **E.** $\dfrac{1}{2}$

9.   121 million

10.   **A.**   20,000

   B.   70,000

   C.   50,000

   D. $\dfrac{2}{5}$ or $\dfrac{5}{2}$ depending on what is compared to what.

   E.   .40 or 2.5 again depending on the comparison.

   F.   30,000

Answers for Chapter Eight

GOAL SETTING EXERCISES (pages 96-97)

1. **A.** $\dfrac{1}{3} = .33\dfrac{1}{3} = 33\dfrac{1}{3}\%$

    B. $\dfrac{2}{5} = .4 = 40\%$

    C. $\dfrac{7}{8} = .875 = 87\dfrac{1}{2}\%$

    D. $\dfrac{5}{6} = .83\dfrac{1}{3} = 83\dfrac{1}{3}\%$

2. **A.** 1:4   **B.** 4:1

    C. 1:8   **D.** 7:1

    E. 4:1   **F.** 5:2 or 2.5:1

    G. 1:3.3

3. **A.** 2:8   **B.** .084

    C. 27   **D.** 2.4

4.

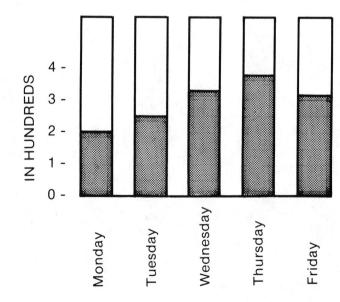

5. 40. Note: This problem is easier to work by common sense than math.

Draw a picture.

6.   **A.** 5   **B.** 3   **C.** 6

   D. 2   **E.** 9

7. 55

8. 400

REACT, PRACTICE, AND EXTEND (page 99)

1. $\frac{5}{10}$ or 1:2

2. 2:5

3. 2:15

4. 7:8

PRACTICE (pages 100-102)

1.   **A.** 1:2   **B.** 1:4   **C.** 6:7   **D.** 5:9

2.   **A.** 1.31 **B.** 5.556 **C.** .12 **D.** $\frac{45}{64}$ **E.** 1.1 (rounded to nearest $\frac{1}{10}$) **F.** 37.8

3.   **A.** 17.9

   B. 2.3

   C. 24.51

   D. .25

VOCABULARY MATCHING (page 103)

1.	K		**7.**	L
2.	F		**8.**	E
3.	H		**9.**	G
4.	A		**10.**	I
5.	B		**11.**	J
6.	C		**12.**	D

CUMULATIVE QUIZ (pages 104-105)

1. **A.** .37609   **B.** 10.028

   C. 19.957   **D.** .216

   E. .108   **F.** .0064

2. **A.** $66.66\frac{2}{3}$ **B.** $3.083\frac{1}{3}$

   C. $29\frac{5}{7}$ **D.** $.0277\frac{7}{9}$

   E. 6750.   **F.** $521.428\frac{4}{7}$

3. **A.** 70.59%   **B.** $141\frac{2}{3}$ %

   C. 7.14%   **D.** 71.43%

   E. 37.5%   **F.** 125%

4. **A.** 8:9

   B. 5:32

   C. 15:4

5. **A.** 8.4

   B. 32

   C. 15.22

6.   **A.**   6.25

    B.   .24

    C.   150

7. $10\dfrac{4}{5}$

8.   20:1   5%

9.   **A.**   7 hits

    B.   24 hits

    C.   86 times at bat

    D.   .293 batting average

    E.   70 times at bat

10. $129\dfrac{1}{6}$

EXTENDING YOUR UNDERSTANDING (page 106)

1. $\dfrac{2}{5}$

2.   1

3.   30¢ and 20¢

4.   50¢

5. $1.00

6. $\dfrac{1}{4}$

7.   3 hours

Answers for Chapter Nine

GOAL SETTING EXERCISE (pages 108-109)

1. **A.** 15.4   **B.** 22.88

   C. 240.10   **D.** 9.28

2. **A.** $471.42\frac{6}{7}$ **B.** 700

   C. 84.932   **D.** $2.33\frac{1}{3}$

3. **A.** 250%   **B.** 37.7%

   C. 40%   **D.** 6.5%

4. **A.** 50%   **B.** 7.2

   C. 244.44

5. 55

6. 104

7. 97.5%

8. 400

REACT, PRACTICE, AND EXTEND (pages 111-113)

1. **A.** $33\frac{1}{3}$%   **B.** 25%

   C. $33\frac{1}{3}$%

2. **A.** 72   **B.** 192

   C. 34.2

3. **A.** 16　　　　　　　　　　**B.** 48

　　C. 60

VOCABULARY MATCHING (page 113)

1. G.　　　　　　　　　　5. B

2. E　　　　　　　　　　6. D

3. F　　　　　　　　　　7. H

4. A　　　　　　　　　　8. C

CUMULATIVE QUIZ (pages 113-114)

1. **A.** 25%　　　　　　　**B.** $33\frac{1}{3}$%

　　C. 11.11%　　　　　　**D.** $133\frac{1}{3}$%

　　E. 6400%　　　　　　**F.** 20%

2. **A.** 6　　　　　　　　**B.** .36

　　C. 5.3　　　　　　　**D.** 51.2

　　E. 6.93　　　　　　　**F.** 3.84

3. **A.** 48　　　　　　　　**B.** 250

　　C. 700　　　　　　　**D.** 25,000

　　E. 90　　　　　　　　**F.** 512

4. 30%

5. 5

6. $9,000.00

7. 87.5%

8. 25%

9. $83\frac{1}{3}$% $16\frac{2}{3}$%

10. 30

EXTENDING YOUR UNDERSTANDING (page 115)

1. A. $\dfrac{24}{96} = \dfrac{N}{100}$ B. $\dfrac{44}{132} = \dfrac{N}{100}$ C. $\dfrac{14}{126} = \dfrac{N}{100}$

   D. $\dfrac{\frac{2}{3}}{.50} = \dfrac{N}{100}$ E. $\dfrac{.48}{.75} = \dfrac{N}{100}$ F. $\dfrac{19}{95} = \dfrac{N}{100}$

2. A. $\dfrac{N}{18} = \dfrac{33\frac{1}{3}}{100}$ B. $\dfrac{N}{2.4} = \dfrac{15}{100}$ C. $\dfrac{N}{26.5} = \dfrac{20}{100}$

   D. $\dfrac{N}{80} = \dfrac{64}{100}$ E. $\dfrac{N}{63} = \dfrac{11}{100}$ F. $\dfrac{N}{96} = \dfrac{4}{100}$

3. A. $\dfrac{12}{N} = \dfrac{25}{100}$ B. $\dfrac{125}{N} = \dfrac{50}{100}$ C. $\dfrac{56}{N} = \dfrac{8}{100}$

   D. $\dfrac{125}{N} = \dfrac{.50}{100}$ E. $\dfrac{27}{N} = \dfrac{30}{100}$ F. $\dfrac{64}{N} = \dfrac{12\frac{1}{2}}{100}$

Answers for Chapter Ten

GOAL SETTING EXERCISE (pages 118-119)

1. **A.** $\dfrac{1}{6}$ **B.** $\dfrac{5}{12}$ **C.** $\dfrac{5}{6}$

   D. $\dfrac{9.5}{12}$ **E.** $\dfrac{7}{6}$ (Don't reduce improper fractions for interest problems.) **F.** $\dfrac{3}{2}$

2. **A.** $63.00 **B.** $26.25 **C.** $176.26

   D. $32.10 **E.** $52.50 **F.** $45.50

3. **A.** 350 **B.** 95

   C. 1,445 **D.** 286.5

4. **A.** $2.84 **B.** $4.97 **C.** $10.93

   D. $14.48 **E.** 22.37

5. $45.84 (Actually $45.83 $\dfrac{1}{3}$, but banks will probably collect the fraction as a whole cent.)

6. $44.00

7. Lose $70.00

8. $900.00 (simple interest)

REACT, PRACTICE, AND EXTEND (pages 122-124)

1. **A.** $307.50 **B.** $447.50

   C. $3,968.00 **D.** $1,911.00

2. **A.** $54,000.00   **B.** $34,100.00

   C. $11,715.00   **D.** $11,685.00

3. Your work should look like this:

A.

$$\frac{\overset{25}{\cancel{\$2,500}}}{1} \times \frac{15}{\cancel{100}_{1}} \times \frac{2}{1} = \$750.00$$

B.

$$\frac{\$18,000}{1} \times \frac{14.5}{100} \times \frac{20}{1} = \frac{\overset{90}{\cancel{\$18,000}}}{1} \times \frac{29}{\cancel{200}_{1}} \times \frac{20}{1} = \text{*}\$52,200.00$$

*This does not necessarily mean that you would pay this much interest on a mortgage of $18,000 for 20 years. Most mortgages are computed on the balance to be paid, so the actual interest over 20 years would be less than $52,200.

C.

$$\frac{\overset{2}{\cancel{200}}}{1} \times \frac{\overset{11}{\cancel{22}}}{\cancel{100}_{1}} \times \frac{1}{2} = \$22.00$$

D.

$$\frac{\overset{5}{\cancel{500}}}{1} \times \frac{15}{\cancel{100}_{1}} \times \frac{3}{2} = \frac{225}{2} = \$112.50$$

4. Example $6.30

  A. $ 6.00 $3.00   50% $ 9.00   30% $ 6.30

  B. $ 7.00 $3.64   52% $10.64   30% $ 7.45

  C. $ 9.30 $4.46   48% $13.76   30% $ 9.63

  D. $11.50 $5.29   46% $16.79   30% $11.75

  E. $10.20 $5.51   54% $15.71   30% $11.00

CUMULATIVE QUIZ (pages 124-127)

1. **A.** 9.12   **B.** $.626\frac{4}{21}$ **C.** 15.645

  D. $5.94\frac{2}{5}$ **E.** 26.66   **F.** $6.26\frac{2}{123}$

2. **A.** 1:3   **B.** $1\frac{3}{4}$:1   **C.** 3:1

   D. 8:9   **E.** $5\frac{1}{5}$:1   **F.** 19:32

3. **A.** N = 9   **B.** N = $15.78\frac{18}{19}$

   C. N = $74\frac{2}{3}$ **D.** N = 1.19

4. **A.** 12.6   **B.** 89

   C. 25.795   **D.** 46

5. **A.** $24.00   **B.** $15.00

   C. $77.00   **D.** $700.00

6. **A.** $37.80   **B.** $100.00   **C.** $79.75

7. $100.00

8. $8,000.00

9. $504.00

10. $3,750.00

EXTENDING YOUR UNDERSTANDING (pages 128-129)

1. Made $300.00. The fact that it was the **same** horse makes no difference. He made $100.00 on each transaction.

2. $1,624.28

3. $3,967.12

Answers for Chapter Eleven

GOAL SETTING EXERCISE (pages 132-133)

1. $A = +2$ $B = -2$ $C = +4$ $D = -4\frac{1}{2}$

2. **A.** 4   **B.** −4
   C. −8   **D.** −18

3. **A.** 52°   **B.** 18°
   C. 72°   **D.** 6°

4. He has $50 left.

5. **A.** −6   **B.** −2
   C. +9   **D.** +8

6. **A.** +36   **B.** +16   **C.** −24
   D. +25   **E.** +5   **F.** −4
   G. −6   **H.** +5   **I.** $+\frac{1}{4}$

7. **A.** +7   **B.** −7
   C. −7   **D.** +7

8. **A.** N = +5   **B.** W = 7
   C. N = 17   **D.** Q = 2.5

9. **A.** −9   **B.** 4
   C. −27   **D.** −10

10. Tuesday

REACT, PRACTICE AND EXTEND (pages 136-137)

1. **A.** +5   **B.** +15   **C.** +4

2. Made $340.45

3. **A.** +8   **B.** −30
    C. +20   **D.** +22

4. **A.** +7   **B.** −34
    C. −24   **D.** −56

5. **A.** +125   **B.** +72
    C. −35   **D.** −32

6. **A.** +3   **B.** +4
    C. −2   **D.** −4

7. **A.** N = 14   **B.** W = 3
    C. Q = 5   **D.** Z = 32

8. **A.** −4   **B.** +1
    C. +3   **D.** +14

VOCABULARY MATCHING (page 138)

1. B.

2. A.

3. E.

4. D.

5. C

ADDITION PRACTICE (page 139)

1. -2	**2.** $+1$	**3.** -16	**4.** $+12$

SUBTRACTION PRACTICE (page 140)

1. -4	**2.** $+17$	**3.** $+9$	**4.** -20

MULTIPLICATION PRACTICE (page 140)

1. $+42$	**2.** $+20$	**3.** -48	**4.** -45

DIVISION PRACTICE (page 141)

1. -8	**2.** $+3$	**3.** $+3$	**4.** $-\dfrac{3}{5}$

PRACTICE (page 142)

1. $W = 6$	**2.** $P = -4$	**3.** $X = -4$	**4.** $Z = 7$

CUMULATIVE QUIZ (pages 142-143)

1.	**A.** $+11$	**B.** -14	**C.** -3	**D.** $+1$
2.	**A.** $+1$	**B.** -19	**C.** $+15$	**D.** $+14$
3.	**A.** -81	**B.** 180	**C.** $+49$	**D.** -25
4.	**A.** $+3$	**B.** $+6$	**C.** -4	**D.** $+\dfrac{1}{3}$
5.	**A.** $+10$	**B.** -72	**C.** -5	**D.** -4

6. $-\$13.43$

7. -15

8. 5

9. $(-20) \times (+6) = -120$
$120 was lost

EXTENDING YOUR UNDERSTANDING (page 144)

A. $(+9) + (-16)$
$+9 + [(-9(+ (-7)]$
$[(+9) + (-9)] + (-7)$
$(0) + (-7)$
-7

B. $(-12) + (+6)$
$[(-6) + (-6)] + (+6)$
$(-6) + [(-6) + (+6)]$
$(-6) + (0)$
-6

C. $(-44) + (+18)$
$[(-26) + (-18)] + (+18)$
$(-26) + [(-18) + (+18)]$
$(-26) + (0)$
-26

D. $(+16) + (-33)$
$(+16) + [(-16) + (-17)]$
$[(+16) + (-16)] + (-17)$
$(0) + (-17)$
-17

Answers for Chapter Twelve

GOAL SETTING EXERCISE (pages 147-149)

1. **A.** 4 **B.** -12 **C.** 5 **D.** -4

2. **A.** $N = -6$ **B.** $N = 0$ **C.** $N = 6$ **D.** $N = 3$

3. **A.** 22 **B.** -5 **C.** $\dfrac{7}{8}$ **D.** -4

4. **A.** 64 **B.** 625 **C.** 49 **D.** 0

5. **A.** $4X$ **B.** $4X^2$ **C.** $2AB$ **D.** $6B^2$

6. **A.** 20 **B.** 4 **C.** -8 **D.** $9X$

7. **A.** 9 **B.** 10 **C.** 15 **D.** $\pm B$*

*Note: This is a peculiar thing about the use of roots. The B^2 is usually considered $+$ or $-$ B since $+B \cdot +B = B^2$ and also $-B \cdot -B$ is B^2. The same is true for the others in this exercise ($-9 \cdot -9 = 81$, $-10 \cdot -10 = 100$). It always works this way but usually is not specified with constants, only variables.

8. 6

9. Sue spent \$12, Martha spent \$7.

10. $A = \dfrac{O}{6}$ (range) or $\dfrac{O}{6}$ (range) $= A$

REACT, PRACTICE AND EXTEND (page 151)

1. **A.** $Q = -5$ **B.** $X = 3$ **C.** $Y = 35$ **D.** $Z = 7$ $Y = 5$

2. **A.** 16 **B.** 106 **C.** 13 **D.** 58

3. **A.** $Y = 3$ **B.** $Y = 6$ **C.** $Y = Z - 3$ **D.** -7

PRACTICE EXAMPLES (page 153)

1. Peaches — 4 cans

   Beans — 12 cans

   Tomatoes — 8 cans

   Here's one way to solve this. (There are many ways.)

   $3P = B$ $2P = T$ $B + P + T = 24$
   Substitute $3P + P + 2P = 24$
   $6P = 24$
   $P = 4$

2. 226.286 cubic inches

   $V = \pi r^2 l$

   $V = \dfrac{22}{7} - 2^2 \cdot 18 = \dfrac{22 \cdot 4 \cdot 18}{7}$

3. 4 and 8

   Let X = the short sides

   $X + 2X + X + 2X = 24$

   $6X = 24$

   $X = 4$

4. 9 girls, 5 boys

   $2B - 1 = G$

   $B + 2B - 1 = 14$

   $3B - 1 = 14$

   $3B = 15$

   $B = 5$

   Check: $9 + 1 = 2 \cdot 5$

PRACTICE EXAMPLES (page 154)

1. 14 **2.** 96 **3.** 67 **4.** 12

INVERSE OPERATIONS PRACTICE EXAMPLES (page 154)

1. $X = 23$ **2.** $X = 7$ **3.** $N = 5$ **4.** $N = 3$

PRACTICE EXAMPLE (page 155)

1. $.89 (3 + 2 + 3) = \$7.12$

PRACTICE EXAMPLES (page 157)

1. $W = 6, V = 2$ **2.** $Z = 8, T = 3$

3. $X = 2\frac{1}{2}, Y = 5$ **4.** $F = -3, G = -4$

PRACTICE EXAMPLES (page 158)

1. $m + n$ **2.** $-6Q - W$

3. $-2m^2 + b^2 - d^2$ **4.** $144 - f - 2a^2$

SQUARE ROOT (pages 158-159)

1. **A.** 29 **B.** 36 **C.** 98 **D.** 59

2. **A.** 216 **B.** 729 **C.** 625 **D.** 1,000,000,000

PYTHAGOREAN THEOREM (page 159)

1. $C^2 = 128$ **2.** $C^2 = 296$ **3.** 144 **4.** 12

VOCABULARY MATCHING (page 159)

1. E

2. D

3. A

4. B

5. C

6. F

CUMULATIVE QUIZ (pages 160-161)

1. **A.** 0   **B.** 5   **C.** −36   **D.** 5

2. **A.** −10   **B.** −3   **C.** 49   **D.** −2

3. **A.** 7.5   **B.** −11   **C.** 44   **D.** $W = 4$

4. **A.** $T = W - C$ **B.** $D = \dfrac{Z - W}{2}$ **C.** $Z = \sqrt{N^2 + B^2}$ **D.** $A = DV$

5. **A.** 22   **B.** 5   **C.** 4   **D.** $\pm B$

6. 17

7. $2.70

8. $9A + 9P + 6O$

EXTENDING YOUR UNDERSTANDING (page 162)

1. **A.** 720,000   **B.** 460,000   **C.** 248.7   **D.** 3200

2. **A.** .025   **B.** .00253   **C.** .0005   **D.** .000002

Answers for Chapter Thirteen

GOAL SETTING EXERCISE (pages 166-168)

1. **A.** V.   **B.** U   **C.** X & Y   **D.** W

   E. Y   **F.** U   **G.** V

2. **A.** Y   **B.** X   **C.** X   **D.** V

   E. All   **F.** U & W   **G.** U, X, & Y

3. **A.** 12   **B.** 8   **C.** 10   **D.** 36

   E. 31.4

4. **A.** 20 sq. in.   **B.** 9 sq. in.   **C.** $7\frac{1}{2}$ sq. in.   **D.** 78.5

5. 216 cubic inches

6. X = 10

7. 81

8. 384 square feet

9. 90°   72°   60°

REACT, PRACTICE AND EXTEND (pages 170-171)

1. **A.** 22°   **B.** < c & d = 135°

2. **A.** 54   **B.** 9

3. **A.** 10.8   **B.** CB = 20

4. **A.** 8.06   **B.** 12.72   **C.** 10.24   **D.** 10

SIMILAR TRIANGLES (page 172)

Fig. 2 14.66

VOCABULARY MATCHING (page 173)

1. C

2. A

3. B

4. F

5. E

6. D

CUMULATIVE QUIZ (pages 173-174)

1. **A.** −39   **B.** −8   **C.** 54   **D.** 33

2. **A.** W = 3   **B.** X = 4   **C.** Y = −2   **D.** $Q = \frac{2}{3}$

3. **A.** 64   **B.** 81   **C.** 256   **D.** 343

4. **A.** 27   **B.** 53   **C.** 13   **D.** 88

5. **A.** $W = \frac{Z}{C}$ **B.** $D = \frac{C}{\pi}$ **C.** $r = \frac{I}{PT}$ **D.** $I = \frac{V}{\pi r^2}$

6. **A.** 51   **B.** 105

7. $5\frac{1}{3}$ ft. (or 5 ft. 4 in.)

8. 36 square feet

Answers for Chapter Fourteen

GOAL SETTING EXERCISE (pages 177-179)

1. **A.** 24 **B.** 7 **C.** 540 **D.** 192

2. **A.** 2 **B.** 3520 **C.** $2\frac{1}{3}$

3. **A.** Cups **B.** Yards **C.** Pounds

4. **A.** 4 square yards **B.** 2 square feet
    C. 864 square inches **D.** $4\frac{2}{3}$ square yards

5. **A.** 3 yds. 1 ft., 6 in. **B.** 3 gal, 1 qt, 1 pt
    C. 1 wk, 3 da, 2 hrs **D.** 2 decades, 5 yrs, 4 mos

6. **A.** 2 gal, 1 qt **B.** 4 hr, 13 min **C.** 13 yds, 2 ft **D.** 1 ton, 1293 pounds

7. 16

8. $104.95

9. $3\frac{1}{2}$ qts = 3 qts, 1 pt for each of the four of them.

10. 1728 cu in equal 1 cubic foot

REACT, PRACTICE, AND EXTEND (pages 181-182)

1. **A.** 15,840 **B.** $20\frac{1}{2}$ **C.** 208 **D.** 420

2. 252 feet

3. **A.** 14 pounds 3 ounces

    B. 41 hours, 38 minutes, 50 seconds or
            1 day, 17 hours, 38 minutes, 50 seconds

    C. 6 weeks, 1 day, 16 hours

    D. 6 decades, 8 years, 2 months

4. **A.** 45 minutes   **B.** 3 tons, 1348 lbs.

    C. 1 yd³ 21 ft³   **D.** 14 yrs., 6 mos.

5. **A.**
$$\begin{array}{r} 4\text{ gal.} \quad 2\text{ qts.} \\ \times \qquad\qquad 8 \\ \hline 32\text{ gal. } 16\text{ qts.} \end{array}$$

$$\begin{array}{r} 32\text{ gal.} \\ 4\text{ gal.} \\ \hline 36\text{ gal.} \end{array}$$

B.
$$\begin{array}{r} 2\text{ yds.} \quad 1\text{ ft.} \\ \times \qquad\qquad 6 \\ \hline 12\text{ yds.} \quad 6\text{ ft.} \end{array}$$

$$\begin{array}{r} 12\text{ yds.} \\ 2\text{ yds.} \\ \hline 14\text{ yds.} \end{array}$$

C.
$$\begin{array}{r} 5\text{ lbs.} \quad 12\text{ oz.} \\ \times \qquad\qquad 9 \\ \hline 45\text{ lbs. } 108\text{ oz.} \end{array}$$

$$\begin{array}{r} 45 \\ +\ 6 \qquad 12\text{ oz.} \\ \hline 51\text{ lbs. } 12\text{ oz.} \end{array}$$

D.
$$\begin{array}{r} 3\text{ hrs. } 16\text{ min.} \\ \times \qquad\qquad 14 \\ \hline 42\text{ hrs. } 224\text{ min.} \end{array}$$

$$\begin{array}{r} 42\text{ hr.} \\ +\ 3\text{ hr. } 44\text{ min.} \\ \hline 45\text{ hr. } 44\text{ min.} \end{array}$$

6. **A.**
$$\begin{array}{r} 1\text{ gal.} \quad 3\text{ qts.} \\ 2\,\overline{)\,3\text{ gal.} \quad 2\text{ qts.}} \\ \underline{2} \\ 1 \times 4 = \underline{4} \\ 6 \\ \underline{6} \end{array}$$

B.
$$\begin{array}{r} 1\text{ yd.} \quad 2\text{ ft.} \\ 4\,\overline{)\,6\text{ yds.} \quad 2\text{ ft.}} \\ \underline{4} \\ 2 \times 3 = \underline{6} \\ 8 \\ \underline{8} \end{array}$$

C. 17 lbs. $1\frac{1}{3}$ oz.

3 $\overline{)\,51$ lbs. 4 oz.

$\underline{51}$

0

4

$\underline{3}$

1

D. 0 $\qquad$ 1 pt.

7 $\overline{)\,3$ qts. 1 pt.

$\underline{0}$

$3 \times 2 = 6$

7

$\underline{7}$

CONVERSION CHARTS (page 184)

1. **A.** 6.944×10^3 or 6944   **B.** 1.34   **C.** 746.27

VOCABULARY MATCHING (page 184)

1. E.

2. C

3. A

4. B

5. D

CUMULATIVE QUIZ (pages 185-186)

1. **A.** −6   **B.** +1   **C.** +8   **D.** −10

2. **A.** +69   **B.** −28   **C.** +3   **D.** −9

3. **A.** Q = 6   **B.** ab = 4   **C.** B = 8   **D.** X = −4

4. **A.** Z = Q −C   **B.** $P = \dfrac{G}{S}$ **C.** $B = \dfrac{2A}{H}$ **D.** $W = (T − X)^2$

5. **A.** 21 square units*   **B.** 88 square units*

$\qquad$ *Since the problem didn't state a unit of measure, yards, feet, etc. the squares are whatever unit is assigned.

6. $192

7. $28.80

8. $4.56

9.   He'll have 10 inches of waste from three boards, and one piece 5 ft., 5 inches long, which is too long to be considered waste.

10.   The simplest way to approach this problem is to first realize $1.20 a foot is 10¢ per inch. Since he had to make seven cuts to get the boards he wanted, he lost $\frac{7}{8}$ inches in saw dust. $\frac{7}{8} \cdot 10¢ = 8\frac{3}{4}¢$

EXTENDING YOUR UNDERSTANDING (pages 187-188)

A.   Miles

B.   Yards

C.   Miles

D.   Inches

E.   Tons (Many tons.) This may surprise you, but look at it and you'll see how impossible the question is. Assume that a teaspoon of sand weighs 1 ounce. (It really doesn't make any difference.) This is a problem of powers. The first day is 2^0 or 1, the second day is 2^1 or 2, the third day is 2^2 or 4, the fourth day 2^3 or 8, then 2^4, 2^5, 2^6 and so on, until the 21st day which is 2^{20}, two to the 20th power or 1,048,576 teaspoons **just** that day. The total amount of sand would be 1 spoon less than 2^{21} or 2.09×10^6 or 65.31 **tons**.

F.   Tons

G.   Ounces — Newborn kangaroos are tiny.

H.   Pounds — Maybe 15 or 16 per month.

I.   Tons — Almost 10 tons. Atmospheric pressure at the Earth's surface is 15 lbs. per square inch. A 36" × 36" card table has a surface area of 1,296 sq. in. Multiply: 1,296 × 15 = 19,440 lbs. or 9.72 tons.

J.   Ounces — But not as many as you think. Gold is weighed in Troy ounces. We use Avoirdupois pounds, so a pound of gold weighs **13.1657** ounces Avoirdupois.

K. Gallons

L. Gallons

M. Gallons — Approximately $12\frac{1}{2}$, depending on your recipe.

N. Pints

Answers for Chapter Fifteen

GOAL SETTING EXERCISE (pages 190-193)

1. **A.** 32¢   **B.** 46¢   **C.** 33¢   **D.** $6.12

2. **A.** 28   **B.** $22\frac{1}{2}$

    C. Sue is four and $\frac{1}{2}$ years younger than her brother.   **D.** $33\frac{1}{2}$

3. The first side is 20" long, the second 28", and the third 8".

4. $2\frac{2}{5}$ days

5. **A.** 24 cubic feet

    B. $52\frac{1}{2}$ cubic inches

    C. 384 cubic feet

    D. 324 cubic feet

6. 12 yards

7. Fill the eight, fill the five from the eight, fill the two from what's left in the eight. There should be one pint left in the eight.

8. 43,560 square feet per acre.

9. 500 hours

10. $\frac{1}{4}$ inch. Page 1 is right next to the last page of volume one. He only has to eat through the cover to get there.

REACT, PRACTICE, AND EXTEND (pages 196-197)

1. $226

2. 3

3. 4 hrs.

4. 10 qts.

5. 90 gal.

6. 55

7. $25

8. 26 mi.

9. 36

10. 36

FORMULAS (pages 198-199)

1. 6600 square yards, including end zones.

2. 100.48 square inches.

3. $88.50 (approximate) each bed. (78.54 square feet × 9 per square foot = 707 ÷ 12 = 59 doz. × $1.50 = $88.50)

4. $169.65. They would probably need to buy 600, which would cost $180.

5.   8.88 yards³   9 cubic yards.

6.   .468 gallon (nearly half)

7.   36 feet

8.   11 feet

VOCABULARY MATCHING (pages 202)

1.   H   8.   N

2.   J   9.   B

3.   L   10. G

4.   C   11. M

5.   I   12. F

6.   E   13. A

7.   K   14. D

CUMULATIVE QUIZ (pages 202-203)

1.   Let X = Martha's debt.
     X = 7200 − 2250 − 850
         X = 4100

2.   **A.** 343   **B.** 16300   **C.** 729   **D.** .026

3.   **A.** 9.8 square inches   **B.** 1 square foot

     C. 5 square feet   **D.** 5 square feet

4.   80.7 feet per second

5.   The four-pound box is slightly cheaper. At the four-pound rate, 6 pounds would
     cost 1.48\frac{1}{2}$.

6. $49

7. $1.68

8. $224

9. 18 feet

10. $12

ALGEBRA RULES

ADDING TWO SIGNED NUMBERS

1. If the number signs are the same, add and use that sign in the answer.

2. If the number signs are different, subtract and use the sign of the larger number as the number sign in the answer.

ALGEBRA RULES

ADDING MORE THAN TWO SIGNED NUMBERS

1. Add all the positive numbers and make a positive total.

2. Add all the negative numbers and make a negative total.

3. Subtract the smaller total from the larger one and give the answer the number sign of the larger total.

ALGEBRA RULES

SUBTRACTING SIGNED NUMBERS

1. Change the sign of the number being subtracted to the opposite sign.

2. Use the rules for adding signed numbers.

ALGEBRA RULES

MULTIPLYING SIGNED NUMBERS

1. If the number signs are the same, multiply, give the answer a positive sign.

2. If the number signs are different, multiply, give the answer a negative sign.

ALGEBRA RULES

DIVIDING SIGNED NUMBERS

1. If the number signs are the same, divide, give the answer a positive sign.

2. If the number signs are different, give the answer a negative sign.

266

ALGEBRA

THE BUILDING BLOCKS

VARIABLES & CONSTANTS

In Algebra, letters are used to represent numbers.
 –In Algebra you write: $X + 8$
 What the answer is depends on the value you assign to X.
 If $X = 2$ then $X + 8 = 10$
 If $X = 7$ then $X + 8 = 15$
 –Since the value of X can *vary* it is called a **variable.**
 –The 8 doesn't change so it is called a **constant.**

ORDER OF OPERATIONS FOR SUBSTITUTION

Simplify parentheses (innermost first)
Compute powers and roots
Multiply or divide
Add or subtract (add Algebraically)*
Divide the denominator
Remember **SCMAD**

*Subtraction in Algebra is usually thought of as adding a negative number.

SUBSTITUTION

In Algebra you often need to replace a variable with a numerical value.
•*Example:* If $A = 4$ and $B = 3$ What is $A + B$?
 Solution: $A + B = 4 + 3 = 7$
•*Example:* If $P = 9$ and $Q = 4$ What is $P - Q$?
 Solution: $P - Q = 9 - 4 = 5$
•*Example:* If $Y = 7$ and $Z = 9$ What is YX?
 Solution: $YX = 7 \bullet 9 = 63$
Note: No operation sign between the letters means to multiply.

SUBSTITUTION WITH MORE THAN ONE OPERATION

•*Example:* If $A = 2$ and $B = 3$ and $C = 5$ What is $A + BC$?
 Solution: $A = BC = 2 + 15 = 17$

SUBSTITUTION OF EQUIVALENT NUMERICAL VALUES OR OTHER VARIABLES

•*Example:* If $A = 5$ and $B = 3$ and $C = 2$ then $A + B + C = (B + C) + B + C = 2B + 2C = 10$

Since $B + C = 5$ and $A = 5$, $B + C$ can be substituted.

•*Example:* If $W = 4$ and $X = W + 4$ then $W + X = W + W + 4 = 2W + 4 = 12$

FORMULAS

Formulas are literal (letters) plans for solving problems. They tell in *general* how to do something. By substitution you can make a formula specific.
 Example: $A = lw$ (Formula for the area of *all* rectangles.)
If the rectangle you want to find the area of is 10″ long and 7″ wide then by substitution:
 Example: $A = 10 \bullet 7 = 70$ square inches.
You have made a general formula specific to your needs.

ALGEBRA

EQUATIONS

An equation is an algebraic statement. It states that the quantities on each side of the equal sign are, in fact, equal.

Example $X + 5 = 7$

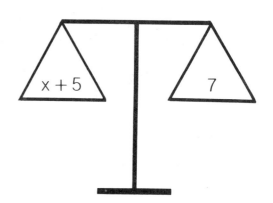

The exact value of **x** to make this statement true is called the **ROOT** or the **SOLUTION**.

$$X + 5 = 7$$

Generally, what you try to do in Algebra is simplify an expression. Usually, this means finding the numerical value for the variables.

$$X + 5 = 7$$
$$X = 2$$

In simple equations this means getting the letters on one side of the equal sign and the numerical value on the other.

INVERSE OPERATIONS

In the equation **$X + 5 = 7$,** the variable is not by itself. Somehow, the 5 must be removed. To find the solution, subtract 5 from **BOTH** sides of the equation because subtraction is the reverse of addition.

- THE INVERSE OF ADDITION IS SUBTRACTION
- THE INVERSE OF SUBTRACTION IS ADDITION*
- THE INVERSE OF MULTIPLICATION IS DIVISION
- THE INVERSE OF DIVISION IS MULTIPLICATION

*Subtraction in Algebra is usually thought of as addition of negative numbers.

EXAMPLES:

$X + 5 = 7$	$Q + 5 = 9$	
Inverse	Inverse	
$-5 -5$	$-5 -5$	
$X = 2$	$Q = 4$	
Substitute	Substitute	
$2 + 5 = 7$	$4 + 5 = 9$	
		$\frac{Q}{3} = 18$
$3W = 21$	$Y - 4 = 12$	Inverse
Inverse	Inverse	$\frac{Q}{3} \times \frac{3}{1} = \frac{18}{1} \times \frac{3}{1}$
$3W \div 3 = 21 \div 3$	$+4 +4$	
$W = 7$	$Y = 16$	$Q = 54$
Substitute	Substitute	Substitute
$3 \bullet 7 = 21$	$16 - 4 = 12$	$54 \div 3 = 18$

ALGEBRA

USING MORE THAN ONE OPERATION TO SOLVE EQUATIONS

Order of operation:

1. Treat addition and subtraction inversely.

2. Then do the multiplication & division.

Example:

$$3Z + 4 = 28$$

(Multiplication) (Addition)

*SUBTRACT $\quad -4 \quad -4$ *(Think inverse of addition)

$$3Z + 0 = 24$$
$$3Z \ = \ 24$$

**DIVIDE $\dfrac{3Z}{3} = \dfrac{24}{3}$ **(Think inverse of multiplication)

$$Z = 8$$

Example: $9 = \dfrac{G}{5} - 1$

ADD $\quad \dfrac{+1 \quad\quad +1}{}$

$$10 = \dfrac{G}{5}$$

MUTIPLY $\ 10 \bullet 5 = \dfrac{G}{5} \bullet 5$

$$50 = G$$

SEPARATED VARIABLES

Combine the variables on each side of the equation before simplifying.

Example: $3X - X + 10 = 24$

COMBINE $\quad 2X + 10 = 24$

SUBTRACT $\quad -10 \quad\quad -10$

DIVIDE $\quad\quad \dfrac{2X}{2} = \dfrac{14}{2}$

$$X = 7$$

Example: $4W - 2 = 2W + 4$

SUBTRACT $\quad \dfrac{-2W \quad\quad -2W}{}$

$\quad\quad 2W - 2 = 4$

ADD $\quad\quad +2 \quad +2$

DIVIDE $\quad\quad \dfrac{2W}{2} = \dfrac{6}{2}$

$$W = 3$$

Example: $30 - 2Q = 2Q + 2$

ADD $\quad \dfrac{+2Q \quad\quad +2Q}{}$

$\quad\quad 30 \quad\quad = 4Q + 2$

SUBTRACT $\ -2 \quad\quad\quad\quad -2$

$\quad\quad\quad \dfrac{28}{4} = \dfrac{4Q}{4}$

DIVIDE

$$7 = Q$$

Example: $\quad \dfrac{2}{3}T = 12$

DIVIDE $\ \dfrac{3}{2} \bullet \dfrac{2}{3}T = \dfrac{12}{1} \bullet \dfrac{3}{2}$

$$T = 18$$

Note: To divide by a fraction, you multiply by the reciprocal.

ALTERNATIVE SOLUTION TO FRACTIONS IN ALGEBRA

Example: $\dfrac{2}{3}T$ is the same as $\dfrac{2T}{3}$; therefore,

$$\dfrac{2T}{3} = 12$$

MULTIPLY $\ \dfrac{2T}{3} \bullet 3 = 12 \bullet 3$

DIVIDE $\quad \dfrac{2T}{2} = \dfrac{36}{2}$

$$T = 18$$

ALGEBRA

LITERAL EQUATIONS

Often in Algebra an equation must be solved that is just letters. You solve by inverse operations to find the requested variable in terms of the other letter.

Example: Solve for C:
$$C - T = W$$
$$\text{ADD} \quad \underline{+T \quad +T}$$
$$C = W + T$$

Example: Solve for B:
$$BQ = X + Y$$
$$\text{DIVIDE} \quad \frac{BQ}{Q} = \frac{X + Y}{Q}$$
$$B = \frac{X + Y}{Q}$$

Example: Solve for L:
$$A = LW$$
$$\text{DIVIDE} \quad \frac{A}{W} = \frac{LW}{W}$$
$$\frac{A}{W} = L$$

This is the formula for the area of a rectangle. Suppose you know the area of a rectangle is 70 square inches, and the width is 7 inches, and you want to find out how long it is. Use the formula above to find the length.

Example:
$$A = LW$$
$$\text{DIVIDE} \quad \frac{70}{7} = \frac{L \bullet 7}{7}$$
$$10 = L$$

270

POWERS AND ROOTS

"THE NEW OPERATIONS"

The **power** of a number tells how many times that number is written in a multiplication problem.

Example: 2^2 Power or exponent

2 Base

Your family tree is an example of the powers of two.

2^1 Parents

2^2 Grandparents

2^3 Great Grandparents

2^4 Greatgreat Grandparents

And so on . . . .

SQUARE	**CUBE**	**SPECIAL CASES**

SQUARE
A number raised to the power of two is read "square." 4^2 is read, "four square."

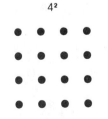

4^2

CUBE
A number raised to the power of 3 is read "cube." 3^3 is read "three cube."

3^3

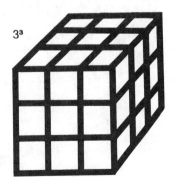

SPECIAL CASES
Any number to the first power is that number.
Example:

$9^1 = 9$

Any number to the power of zero is one.
Example:

$12^0 = 1$

Zero power means, "Divided by itself."
Example:

$12^0 = {}^{12}/_{12} = 1$

SQUARE ROOT

SQUARE ROOT

Extracting the square root of a number means to find the number that, when multiplied by itself, gives the original number.

EXAMPLE: Find the square root of 25 ($\sqrt{25}$)

$\sqrt{25} = 5$ because $5 \cdot 5 = 25$

AVERAGING METHOD

Find $\sqrt{576}$

Step 1. Guess a round number that is fairly close to the correct answer. In this case 40 would be a bad guess because 40×40 would be 1600. 20 would be a better guess because 20×20 is 400 and 30×30 equals 900. You know the correct square is somewhere between. 20 is closer so use it in step 2.

Step 2. Divide your guess into the number you are finding the square root of.

$$
\begin{array}{r}
28 \\
20\overline{\smash{)}576} \\
40 \\
\hline
176 \\
160 \\
\hline
16
\end{array}
$$

Step 3. Ignoring the remainder, average the quotient and the divisor.

$$
\begin{array}{r}
28 \\
+\,20 \\
\hline
48
\end{array}
$$

$$
\begin{array}{r}
24 \\
2\overline{\smash{)}48}
\end{array}
$$

Step 4. Multiply this average times itself. If you made a good estimate, you will have the square root.

$24 \times 24 = 576$

24 is the square root of 576

What happens if your estimate is wrong?

$$50\overline{\smash{)}576} \quad 50 + 11 = 61 \quad 2\overline{\smash{)}61}$$

(with 11 above 576 and 30 above 61)

50 is not the square root of 576. So try again, using 30 as the estimate.

STANDARD METHOD

Find $\sqrt{576}$

Step 1. If the number is a whole number, place a decimal point at the right of the units column.

$$\sqrt{576.}$$

(If it is already expressed as a decimal fraction, this is unnecessary.)

Step 2. Starting at the decimal point and counting to the left, break up the number in groups of two digits.

$$\sqrt{5\ 76}$$

Step 3. Find the largest root number whose square is less than the leftmost group. (In this case, the number is 2, since $2 \times 2 = 4$.)

$$\overset{2}{\sqrt{5\ \ 76}}$$

Step 4. Square the 2 and write the answer underneath the first group of numbers. Then subtract and bring down the next pair of numbers.

$$
\begin{array}{r}
5\ \ 76 \\
-\,4 \\
\hline
1\ \ 76
\end{array}
$$

Step 5. Now you must do a division problem. Your new bottom line (176) is the dividend. *Double* the *top* line of the problem and write it down as the divisor leaving a blank space for another digit.

$$4\_\,\overline{\smash{)}176}$$

The "missing digit" will also be the next digit in the answer to the original problem. Estimate what this digit is by dividing 4 into the first two digits of the divisor (17).

$$
\begin{array}{r}
4 \\
44\overline{\smash{)}176} \\
176
\end{array}
$$

Step 6. *Multiply* to check your estimate ($4 \times 44 = 176$). If you subtract and get 0, you're finished. Write the answer as the next part of the square root.

$$
\begin{array}{r}
2\quad 4 \\
\sqrt{5\ \ 76}
\end{array}
$$

$$
\begin{array}{r}
4 \\
44\overline{\smash{)}1\ \ 76} \\
1\ \ 76 \\
\hline
0
\end{array}
$$

GEOMETRY

Ancients studied Geometry using only two tools, a compass and an unmarked straight edge.

It was from this simple beginning that the entire study of Geometry grew. Here are some of the ideas that have come down to us from those ancient times. We still play by their rules.

THE POINT

A spot in space that has no dimension and only one location.

THE RAY

A ray starts at a point and extends to infinity in one direction.

THE LINE

The line, unlike the ray, extends in both directions to infinity. It has only length, no width.

When you draw what you call "a line," it is only a representation because what you draw has width. A line is an idea and can't really be seen.

LINE SEGMENT

A segment is a part of a line. It has a point of beginning and a point of ending.

ANGLE

An angle is made up of two rays with a common origin. The place where the rays come together is called the vertex. A is the vertex.

INTERSECTING LINES

To intersect means to cross. This describes two lines that have a point in common.

PERPENDICULAR LINES

Lines that intersect to form a right angle (90°) at the point of intersection are called perpendicular lines.

PARALLEL LINES

Parallel lines are lines that would never intersect if they were on a flat surface (a plane).

PLANE

A plane is an imaginary flat surface that extends to infinity in all directions. Plane geometry takes its name from this concept, and in plane geometry, the figures have only two dimensions, length and width, but no thickness..

SOLID GEOMETRY

In solid geometry, a figure is considered solid if it has three dimensions, length, width and depth.

GEOMETRY

TOOLS OF THE TRADE

In Geometry, where a drawing is often made to represent a figure, some precision is needed.

The basic tools are a compass and an unmarked straight edge.

Another tool you will need is the protractor. This device measures angles.

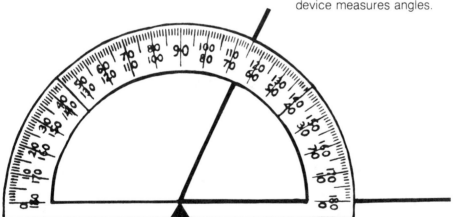

Angles are measured in degrees, minutes and seconds. There are sixty minutes in a degree and sixty seconds in a minute, just like seconds in minutes and minutes in hours.

In the illustration above, the angle being measured is 65°.

Notice on the protractor, two readings are possible at the same point. An obtuse angle of 115″ would be read at the same place on the protractor as an acute angle of 65″.

KINDS OF ANGLES

STRAIGHT ANGLE
A straight angle is 180°.

RIGHT ANGLE
Angle ABC is a right angle. It measures 90°.
Angle DBC is also a right angle. It takes angles
ABC and DBC to equal a straight angle. Notice
the symbol ⌐. This is a specialized symbol, reserv-
ed exclusively for right angles.

ACUTE ANGLE
An angle of less than 90° is an acute angle.
ABC is an acute angle.

OBTUSE ANGLE
An angle that measures more than 90° is obtuse.
ABC is an obtuse angle.

GEOMETRY

POLYGONS

In plane geometry, polygon is the general term for any closed figure containing more than one angle and side. Many of these figures have special names, but others don't.

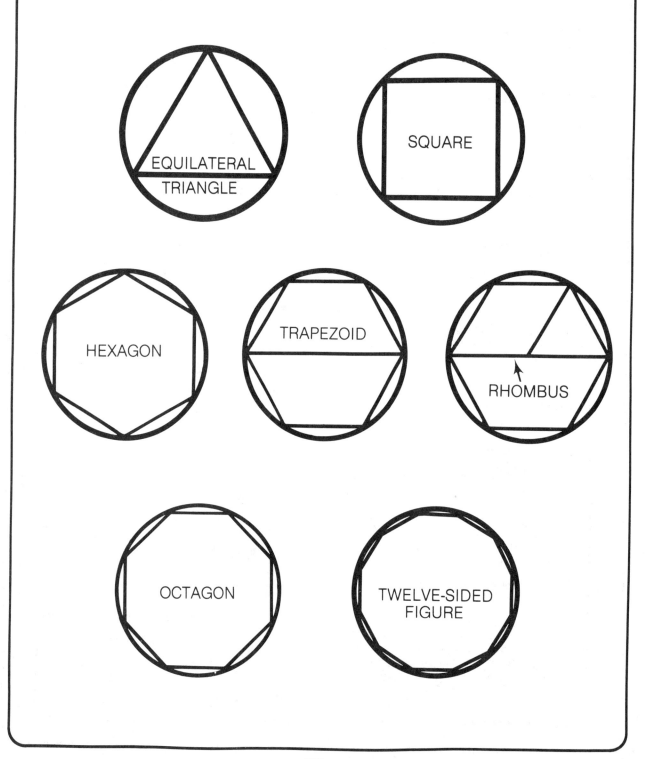

EQUILATERAL TRIANGLE

SQUARE

HEXAGON

TRAPEZOID

RHOMBUS

OCTAGON

TWELVE-SIDED FIGURE

GEOMETRY

TRIANGLES

SCALENE
If a triangle has no sides the same length it is scalene.

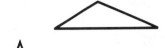

ISOSCELES
If a triangle has two sides the same length it is isosceles.

EQUILATERAL
If all sides of a triangle are the same length the triangle is equilateral.

ACUTE
If a triangle has three acute angles the triangle is acute.

EQUIANGULAR
If the actue angles are all the same the triangle is equiangular. If it is equiangular it is also equilateral.

RIGHT TRIANGLE
If one angle of a triangle is 90°, the triangle is a right triangle. There can be only one right angle in a triangle.

OBTUSE
If a triangle has an obtuse angle the triangle is obtuse.

ALTITUDE OF A TRIANGLE

 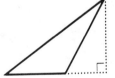

An altitude of a triangle is a line segment drawn from any vertex so that it is perpendicular to the side opposite that vertex. (Sometimes it is necessary to extend the base line to find the altitude as in Fig. 2.)
In the right triangle in Fig. 3, the side adjacent to the right angle is the altitude.

FORMULAS
Perimeter of = P = S + S + S
Area of = A = ½B•H

277

GEOMETRY

RECTANGLES AND SQUARES

Rectangles and squares are figures with four sides and four right angles.

RECTANGLE

If a figure has four right angles, the sides must be parallel. Because of the 90° angles, the sides opposite one another must be equal (congruent).

Rectangles are often defined as parallelograms with four right angles whose diagonals are congruent.

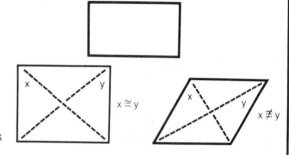

SQUARE

A square is a specialized rectangle in which *all* the sides are equal (congruent).

All the rules that apply to rectangles apply to squares.

1. sides parallel

2. four right angles

3. diagonals are congruent

PERIMETER

Perimeter is the measure of the distance around a figure. In figure 1 (rectangle) the distance around it can be thought of as $X + Y + X + Y$ or as $2X + 2Y$ or $X + Y$ times 2.

In figure 2 (square) the perimeter can be thought of as $S + S + S + S$ or $4 \times S$.

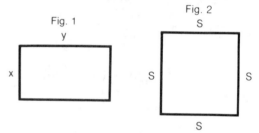

Fig. 1

Fig. 2

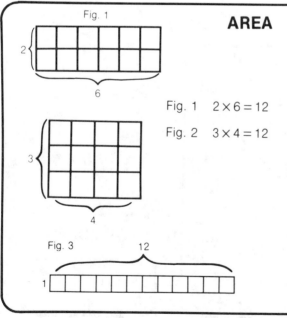

Fig. 1

Fig. 1 $2 \times 6 = 12$

Fig. 2 $3 \times 4 = 12$

Fig. 3

AREA

Area is measured in "area units." This is generally a "square" of some kind. It can be square inches, square feet, square yards, square centimeters, square miles, etc.

The area of a rectangle is the number of area units that are contained within the figure.

Each square in the rectangles represented is an area unit. Each one can stand for any measure. Both figures contain twelve area units. The area of a rectangle can be found by multiplying the units along one side by the units on an adjacent side.

Perimeter and area are related. Figures 1 and 2 to the left have the same area, but the perimeter of figure 1 is 16 and the perimeter of figure 2 is 14.

Look at Fig. 3 to the left. This rectangle has an area of 12 units, also. The perimeter of this figure is 26.

The more nearly square a rectangle is, the greater the area in relationship to the perimeter.

GEOMETRY

CONSTRUCTIONS

Bisecting a line segment with a straight edge and a compass. (Bisecting means cutting a line segment into two equal pieces.)

STEP 1
Draw an arc (a segment of a circle) that is more than half the length of the segment. Without changing the setting of the compass, draw another arc from the other end. Make the arcs long enough so they cross at two points.

STEP 2
Use a straight edge and line up the two intersecting points of the arcs. Set a point where the straight edge crosses the line to determine the middle of the line segment or draw a line to construct a perpendicular.

COPYING AN ANGLE
Problem: Copy angle OQC.

STEP 1 Draw line Q′ C′. (The mark above the letters indicates the lines are "like" the originals, but not the originals. It is read, Q prime, C prime.

STEP 2 With a compass, draw an arc from the vertex of ∠ OQC. Draw an arc with the same radius on Q′ C′.

STEP 3 Using the compass again on ∠ OQC, measure the distance where the rays of the angle intersect the arc you have just drawn

STEP 4 Transfer this distance to Q′ C′ and draw a small arc.

STEP 5 Draw a line from Q′ so it passes through point X.
The angle you have drawn is like the original. It is said to be congruent. The symbol ≅ means congruent.

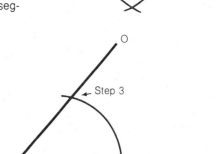

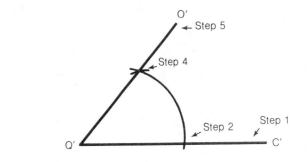

BISECTING AN ANGLE

An angle can be cut into two (or powers of 2) pieces with a compass and a straight edge much the same way that a line can.

PROBLEM: Bisect ∠ DFZ.

STEP 1 Draw an arc at vertex F.

STEP 2 On this arc, draw two arcs that are over half the distance of the first arc drawn.

STEP 3 Draw a line from the vertex that passes through the intersect points of these arcs.

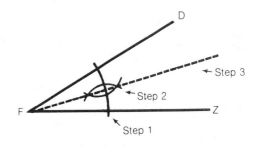

GEOMETRY

THE PYTHAGOREAN THEOREM

One of the most famous statements in geometry is:
"The square on the side of the hypotenuse is equal to the sum of the squares on the other two sides."
Algebraically, we explain the formula this way:

$$C^2 = A^2 + B^2$$
To find C:
$$C^2 = 4^2 + 3^2$$
$$C^2 = 16 + 9$$
$$C^2 = 25$$
$$C = \sqrt{25}$$
$$C = 5$$
$$B^2 = C^2 - A^2$$
$$A^2 = C^2 - B^2$$

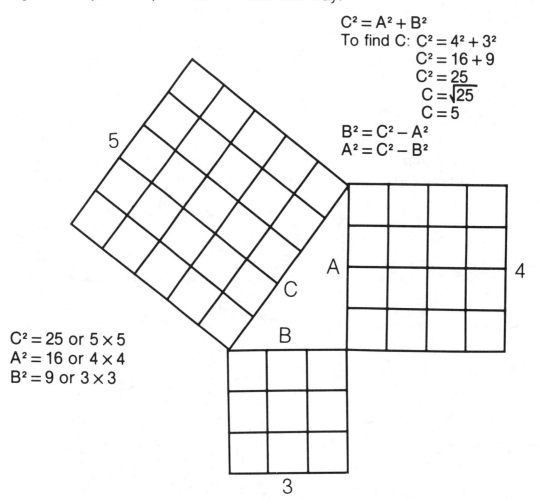

$C^2 = 25$ or 5×5
$A^2 = 16$ or 4×4
$B^2 = 9$ or 3×3

By substitution, any one of the sides can be found if the lengths of the other two are known.

$A = \sqrt{16}$ or $16 + B^2 = 25$
$A = 4$ $B^2 = 25 - 16$
                                       $B^2 = 9$
                                       $B = \sqrt{9}$
                                       $B = 3$

GEOMETRY

CIRCLES
A circle is a curved line that starts and ends at the same point never crossing itself and passing through a series of points that are all the same distance from a point called the center.

Parts of a Circle

Diameter: A straight line through the center connecting points on opposite sides of the circle.

Radius: A straight line that connects the center to a point on the circle. (2 times the radius equals the diameter.)

Circumference: The distance around the circle. It is like the perimeter of other straight line figures, but it has the special name of circumference.

Pi: To solve problems using circles π must be used. Pi is a Greek letter that stands for the ratio between the circumference and the diameter. This ratio is the same for all circles. If you were considering a circle twenty-two feet in circumference, the diameter would be seven feet. Pi is sometimes expressed as $^{22}\!/_7$ or $3\frac{1}{7}$ but usually as a decimal, 3.1416.*

*$^{22}\!/_7$ is not exact. All expressions of Pi are approximations.

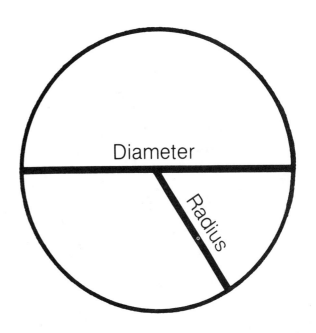

Formulas for Circles
Circumference = π diameter
Area = $\pi\, r^2$ (radius squared)
Area of a circle is always expressed in squares.

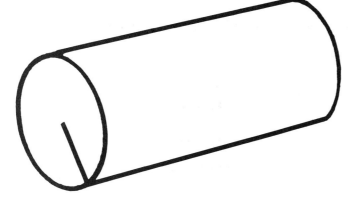

Volume of a Circular Solid
Volume of a cylinder
$V = \pi \bullet r^2 \bullet L$

Step 1
Find the area of the circular cross section (area equals Pi times the radius squared).

Step 2
Multiply by the length.
Volume of a circular solid is expressed as cubes.

GEOMETRY

RECTANGULAR SOLIDS

Area
applies to the number of squares (area units) it takes to fill a figure on a single plane.

Volume
refers to the number of cubes it takes to fill a three-dimensional figure.

Fig. 1

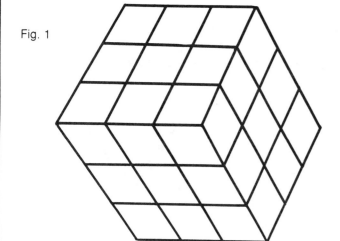

Looking at figure 1, it is easy to see that the large cube is filled with smaller ones. The area of one surface would be 3 × 3 or 9 *but,* there are three such stacks of smaller cubes making up the larger one.
Therefore 3 × 3 × 3 or 27 is the volume of this cube.

The volume of the rectangular solid in figure 2 (and all other such solids) can be found by multiplying the three dimensions together.
2 × 2 × 5 = 20

Fig. 2

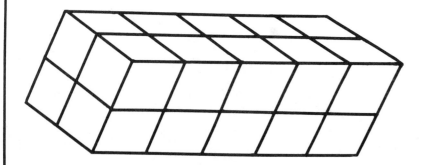

GLOSSARY

Absolute Value — The numerical "bigness" of a number; its distance from zero. *(Chapter 11)*

Abstract — Imaginary; having no concrete existence. *(Chapter 7)*

Acute — An angle that measures fewer than 90 degrees. *(Chapter 13)*

Additive Quality — Multiplication can be thought of as a series of additions. Its inverse, division, can be thought of as a series of subtractions. *(Chapter 5)*

Altitude — A line drawn from any vertex of a triangle perpendicular to the opposite side. It is used to find the height of the triangle. *(Chapter 13)*

Angle — The figure formed where two lines intersect. *(Chapter 13)*

Annexing Zeroes — Placing extra zeroes in a decimal where they are needed to allow the decimal point to be where it belongs. *(Chapter 7)*

Arc — A section of the circumference of a circle. *(Chapter 13)*

Area — The amount of surface a plane figure contains. *(Chapter 13)*

Assessed Evaluation (Value) — The amount on which property taxes are charged, usually computed in some way from the value of the property. *(Chapter 10)*

Axis — A horizontal (parallel to the ground) or vertical (up and down) line drawn as a starting point for a graph. *(Chapter 7)*

Balance — Equations must always "balance" — the quantities on both sides of the equal sign must be equal. *(Chapter 8)*

Base — In a triangle, the line from which the other lines and angles are measured. *(Chapter 13)*

Cancellation — In multiplication and division of fractions, a process of simplifying the problem so it can be solved more easily. *(Chapter 6)*

Circle — A curved closed line whose points are all the same distance from a point called the center. *(Chapter 13)*

Circumference — The distance around a circle. *(Chapter 4)*

Co-efficient — The number part of an expression such as 3X. *(Chapter 12)*

Colon — The punctuation mark (:). It is used in ratio problems instead of the line used in a fraction. *(Chapter 8)*

Common Denominator — When two fractions have the same lower term (denominator), they are said to have a "common denominator." *(Chapter 1)*

Common Factor — A number that will divide both terms of a fraction. *(Chapter 1)*

Common Fraction — Any expression that represents a quantity less than one or a sharing of numbers that is less than 1/1. *(Chapter 1)*

Compass — An instrument used to draw circles. *(Chapters 4 & 13)*

Compound Fraction — A fraction within a fraction. *(Chapter 6)*

Concrete — Having real, physical existence. *(Chapter 7)*

Congruent — The same; equal. Two figures are "congruent" if their shape and dimensions are all the same. *(Chapter 13)*

Constant — A quantity whose value does not change during computation. *(Chapter 12)*

Conversion — Expressing measures in different units. *(Chapter 14)*

Cost Price — The amount stores pay for the items they sell. *(Chapter 10)*

Cross-Multiplication — A method in which the numerator of one fraction is multiplied by the denominator of another. *(Chapters 2 & 8)*

Cube — A solid whose six faces are all congruent squares. *(Chapter 13)*

Cubic Measure — Volume is measured by counting the number of cubes of a certain size necessary to completely fill a solid. *(Chapter 14)*

Decimal Fractions — A fraction whose denominator is 10 or a multiple of 10. *(Chapter 7)*

Decimal Understood — At the end of every whole number is a decimal point, even if it isn't written. *(Chapter 7)*

Degrees — The units in which angles are measured. A circle contains 360 degrees. The symbol ( ) means "degrees." *(Chapter 13)*

Denominator — The bottom term of a fraction. It gives the "name" to that fraction. *(Chapter 1)*

Diameter — The distance across a circle measured through the center. *(Chapter 4)*

Discount — The difference between the usual selling price and the sale price. *(Chapter 10)*

Discount Rate — The percentage of the selling price that is subtracted to get the sale price. *(Chapter 10)*

Dividend — In a division problem, the number to be divided. *(Chapter 5)*

Divisor — In a division problem, the number to be divided by. *(Chapter 5)*

English System — The system of measurement most commonly used in the United States (feet, quarts, yards, etc.). *(Chapter 14)*

Equal — Equivalent in value; expressing the same quantity. *(Chapter 11)*

Equation — A statement of equality. It means that the quantities on both sides of the equal sign are the same. *(Chapter 9)*

Equilateral/Equiangular — A triangle with all three sides the same length and all three angles equal to 60 degrees. *(Chapter 13)*

Euclid — A Greek mathematician who lived around 300 B.C. He organized the basic rules of the geometry we still use today, which is sometimes called Euclidean Geometry. *(Chapter 13)*

Factor — A number that will divide another number evenly. *(Chapter 1)*

Formula — A plan for solving problems. *(Chapter 9)*

General Case Statement — A plan that can be used to solve all addition and subtraction of fractions problems. *(Chapter 2)*

Girth — A term used by the post office; the perimeter of the smallest dimension of a package. *(Chapter 14)*

Graph — A picture of numerical information. *(Chapter 7)*

Greater Than/Less Than — The symbols > and <. > is read "is greater than" and < is read "is less than." *(Chapter 3)*

Gross Profit — The simple difference between the cost price and the selling price. *(Chapter 10)*

Hypotenuse — The side opposite the right angle in a right triangle; the longest side of a right triangle. *(Chapter 13)*

Identity Element — A number that enters into the computation but has no effect on the outcome. *(Chapter 2)*

Increment — A division on a graph; a section of a line or a measurement. *(Chapter 7)*

Inductive Reasoning — A method of looking at the parts of something and making a judgment about what the whole must be. *(Chapter 2)*

Infinite — Endless. *(Chapter 3)*

Infinity — The theoretical place where the numbers end. *(Chapter 1)*

Interest — Money that money makes. If you have a savings account, you earn interest. If you borrow money, you pay interest. *(Chapter 10)*

Intuition — A quality of the mind that allows you to know something without knowing why. *(Chapter 6)*

Inverse — Opposite or backward. The inverse of addition is subtraction, and the inverse of multiplication is division. *(Chapters 3 & 5)*

Invert — To turn upside down. *(Chapter 5)*

Linear Measure — A measure of length only. A line has length but no width or thickness. *(Chapter 14)*

Literal Equation — An algebraic statement that uses letters to represent quantities. *(Chapter 12)*

Margin — Same as mark-up or gross profit. *(Chapter 10)*

Market Value — The actual value of a property; the amount it would sell for. *(Chapter 10)*

Mark-Up — The amount stores add to the cost price to get the selling price. *(Chapter 10)*

Mark-Up Rate — The percentage of the cost price added to get the selling price. *(Chapter 10)*

Metric System — A decimal system of measurement used instead of the English system in most of the world. *(Chapter 14)*

Minus — The minus sign (-) indicates the operation of subtraction or a negative number. *(Chapter 11)*

Multiplicand — In a multiplication problem, the number to be multiplied. *(Chapter 5)*

Multiplier — In a multiplication problem, the number to be multiplied by. *(Chapter 5)*

Negative Numbers — Numbers less than zero. *(Chapter 3)*

Number Line — A picture of the number system. *(Chapter 3)*

Number Sign — A symbol indicating whether a number is positive (+) or negative (-). *(Chapter 11)*

Numeral — A way of expressing the idea of number. *(Chapter 3)*

Numerator — The top number of a fraction. It represents the number of pieces being considered. *(Chapter 1)*

Obtuse — An angle greater than 90 degrees. *(Chapter 13)*

Opposite of — A number with the same absolute value but a different sign. *(Chapter 11)*

Parallel — Two lines drawn so that they are always the same distance from each other are "parallel." *(Chapter 13)*

Percent — A specialized decimal meaning "out of 100." *(Chapter 7)*

Perimeter — The distance around a plane geometric figure. *(Chapter 13)*

Perpendicular — Two lines that meet to form a right angle (90 degrees) are "perpendicular." *(Chapter 13)*

Pi — The fractional relationship of the circumference to the diameter of a circle. *(Chapter 4)*

Place Value — In our number system, each place or column has a value that is 10 times the value of the column to its right and one-tenth the value of the column to its left. *(Chapter 7)*

Plane — An imaginary flat surface with length and width but no depth. Any three points are contained in one plane, just as any two points can be connected by one line. (Chapter 13)

Plus — The plus sign (+) indicates the operation of addition or a positive number. *(Chapter 11)*

Polygon — A word meaning "many sides"; the general name given to plane figures. *(Chapter 13)*

Positive Numbers — Numbers greater than zero. *(Chapter 3)*

Power — A number being multiplied by itself. *(Chapter 12)*

Power of Ten — Tens multiplied by tens. *(Chapter 7)*

Principal — The amount you borrow or the amount on which interest is paid or earned. *(Chapter 10)*

Product — The answer or result of a multiplication problem. *(Chapter 5)*

Profit — The amount of the gross profit left after all expenses are subtracted. *(Chapter 10)*

Proportion — A way of thinking about two ratios. It answers a question like "Two is to three as what is to nine?" *(Chapters 8 & 14)*

Protractor — A device used to measure the sizes of angles. *(Chapter 13)*

Pythagoras — A mathematician and philosopher who lived 2,500 years ago. *(Chapter 13)*

Pythagorean Theorem — The statement that, in a right triangle, the square of the length of the hypotenuse is equal to the sum of the squares of the lengths of the other two sides. *(Chapter 13)*

Quotient — The answer or result of a division problem. *(Chapter 5)*

Radius — The distance from the center of a circle to a point on the circle; it is equal to half the diameter of the circle. *(Chapter 13)*

Rate — The percentage paid or earned as interest, usually over a given period of time. *(Chapter 10)*

Ratio — Comparing numbers by the process of division. *(Chapters 7 & 14)*

Rational Number Family — A series of fractions that are equal to one another. Also called a fraction family. *(Chapter 1)*

Real Number — Any number that describes the distance from zero. *(Chapter 11)*

Reciprocal — A number that can be multiplied by another number to get 1. *(Chapter 6)*

Rectangle — A four-sided polygon with four right angles. *(Chapter 13)*

Reducing to Lowest Terms — Expressing a fraction with the simplest representation possible. When a fraction is in lowest terms, the numerator and denominator have no common factor other than 1. *(Chapter 2)*

Reference Point — In graphs, any point that can be identified numerically. *(Chapter 7)*

Regrouping — Expressing a quantity in a different way so it is more useful for the purpose of computing. *(Chapter 3)*

Requested Unknown — The variable you are asked to solve for (find the value of). *(Chapter 12)*

Right angle — An angle measuring 90 degrees. *(Chapter 13)*

Right triangle — A triangle with one angle of 90 degrees. *(Chapter 13)*

Root — The opposite of power; a number that can be multiplied by itself to get another number. *(Chapter 12)*

Selling price — The amount you pay for items in a store. *(Chapter 10)*

Sequence of Operations — In a series of different operations, the order in which they are to be performed. *(Chapter 12)*

Signed Numbers — Numbers that contain a positive or negative sign as part of the quantity they express. *(Chapter 11)*

Simplify — 1. To reduce a ratio to its lowest possible terms. *(Chapter 8)*
    2. To rewrite a numerical statement of equality as simply as possible. *(Chapter 11)*
    3. To find the simplest units of measure in which an answer can be expressed. *(Chapter 14)*

Simultaneous Equations — A process of solving for more than one unknown by comparing two statements of equality. *(Chapter 12)*

Solid — A figure with depth as well as length and width. *(Chapter 13)*

Square — A rectangle with all four sides the same length. *(Chapter 13)*

Square Measure — In measuring area, you count the number of squares of a given size necessary to completely cover a surface. *(Chapter 14)*

Substitution — Calling a mathematical quantity by a different name to simplify computations. *(Chapter 11)*

Taxable Amount — The amount taxes are assessed on. *(Chapter 10)*

Time — In working with interest, the period over which interest is paid or earned. *(Chapter 10)*

Unequal — Not equivalent; not expressing the same quantity. *(Chapter 11)*

Unlike Denominators — When two fractions have different bottom terms (denominators), they are said to have "unlike denominators." *(Chapter 1)*

Variable — A term (usually a letter) in an algebraic statement that can be assigned any value. *(Chapter 12)*

Vertex — A point where two lines or line segments meet to form an angle. *(Chapter 13)*

Volume — The number of cubes of a given size contained within a solid. *(Chapter 13)*

Zero — The only number that is neither positive nor negative. *(Chapter 11)*